300

The
MYSTERY OF SEX
and
RACE REGENERATION

A Sane, Sensible and Reasonable Approach to the Highly Important but
Much Involved Problem of Sex from the Natural, Moral and Religious
Aspects and Having the REgeneration of the Race in View.

By
R. SWINBURNE CLYMER, M.D.
College of Medicine and Surgery
Chicago, 1902

Author of: "The Natura Physician," "Natura Medicine," "The Thomsonian
System of Medicine," "The International System of Direct Medication," "Diet,
A Key to Health," "Dietary Guide," "Pre-Natal Influence," etc.

Published by
THE PHILOSOPHICAL PUBLISHING COMPANY
Beverly Hall
QUAKERTOWN, PENNA.

9/98

FOREWORD

Fourth Edition

*Co-ordinated Special American, Central American (Spanish)
and South American (Portuguese) Edition*

INCE the publication of the fourth English edition and
the several editions of this work in Spanish in the
South American countries, a completely new approach
has become necessary as a reinterpretation of the laws
governing creative (sex) activity from a sound
physical, moral and spiritual standpoint.

Up until that time, in fact, until a very short time ago,
humanity as a whole was submerged in sex ignorance, though
the more enlightened were usually governed by inhibitions
and taboos.

This was due to the fact that actual knowledge on sex
subjects has been at a premium. Educators as a class are as
ignorant as the mass.

The church, whose duty it was, and still is, to teach mankind the laws governing moral and spiritual behavior—sex
coming under both categories—ignored, and continues to ignore, this all-important most vital subject.

It is true, of course, that shortly after the first world war,
novelists, almost as a whole, sensing the degeneration of morality which had taken place during the war, seized upon sex
and the worst of its characteristics, as themes for their novels.

Never before in the history of the world was mankind fed
with so much immoral filth as during the past twenty-five

years. In the almost multitudinous novels with their varied
themes, all dealing with the dark side of sex, virtually every
phase of debased sex thought and practice was dealt with.

As was only natural, the millions of men and women who
constantly read this debasing literature were inoculated with
an inner defilement which gradually, imperceptibly and almost
unconsciously, took place.

Today many of these millions are almost unable to look
squarely into the eyes of even those they love, or believe they
love, because of the contaminated thoughts and inner desires
governing them.

During all of the past centuries there has been only one
publication which could compare in its evil, debasing, degrading sex teachings, to these novels taken as a whole.

This was Le KAMA SOUTRA Regles de L'Amour de Vat-
syayana, a work translated into French, but considered so evil in
its inculcations and influence that its importation, even though
published in French, was forbidden.

This work, giving instructions in all the vile practices known
to man, did not actually have as evil an influence on humanity
as our modern sex novels. This is explained in the fact that
basically, it was a religious work and a strong psychological
factor was present.

This factor was missing in our modern novels, the base side
being paramount; the evil, sensual side was dramatized as the
only important subject under consideration.

This lowering of the moral thought, sense and desire of the
vast number of peoples as a direct result of these debased publications gave rise to another evil, which, if possible, has had,
and continues to have, an almost greater influence for debasement than the "sexy" novels.

We have reference to the madness for the so-called *surveys* so much publicized, bringing to public attention what was and has always been considered the private affair of husband and wife.

The practices taught and explained in *Kama Soutra* were, as mentioned, basically considered as religious practices. These practices were as evil as a debased humanity can make anything evil; nevertheless, the psychological religious thought held a subduing influence over those given to the practice. BY NO POWER OF THE IMAGINATION CAN THIS BE SAID OF THE MODERN NOVELS OR OF THE EXPOSITIONS IN THE SURVEYS.

The state of mind in general of those engaged in these surveys is all too clearly indicated by a statement on the part of one of the men interested in the SURVEYS and which is here quoted:

"The sexual behavior of people is based on a great many different traditions, superstitions, impulses and individual experiences[1]. But our attitudes toward sex are not even as reasonable as our behavior.

"The Greeks inhabited a rather unproductive land and, at

---

[1] We have no quarrel with this statement, though it is far from complete. To the reasons for sexual behavior should be added, above all—IGNORANCE ON THE PART OF THE MASS. The fact that men are inherently possessed of a mighty (biological) urge; an all-controlling desire; without knowledge of how to correctly apply, direct and use it.

All of this is due to the fact that those appointed, or who appointed themselves, to teach and guide mankind, have failed to do so. Mankind has honestly believed, and still believes, that sex belongs to the dark side of life, the gutter, and is to be hidden and not brought to light, whereas it is of the highest, deepest spiritual significance and importance.

It rests on a moral foundation; having within it the power to debase and degrade; to degenerate and destroy, or to elevate, exalt and REgenerate all mankind, *i.e.,* spiritualize and *lift up*, as Moses did the serpent in the wilderness.

The church, above all others, has been, and still is, recreant in its holy duty, despite the fact that in its Scriptures are all the instructions needed, and only require proper, correct, and enlightened interpretation.

the height of their glory, there were a great many of them per square mile. They were intelligent enough to realize that all of them would suffer if their population grew so rapidly that mouths multiplied faster than their resources[2]. The result was a set of sexual customs which positively discouraged reproduction. As a last resort they employed infanticide, but they preferred less obviously harsh measures.

"Therefore, homosexuality[3] was an accepted outlet for the sexual outlet of both men and women. A Greek gentleman was thought a little queer, not quite respectable, if he did not keep a male lover. In addition, a highly regarded class of women was developed, a sort of supermistress, with whom Greek men could have extra-marital relations without fear of consequences[4] either in the way of undesirable offspring or social ostracism.

"Homosexuality among women was so equally recognized as a proper sexual outlet that the Greek island of Lesbos gave its name to the practice. Among the Greeks it was not a word which needs to be said in whispers or behind the hand.

---

[2] This idea in itself is a sound and practical one. The entire world is facing this problem now and unless *wise* measures are taken, famine will stalk the world within another fifty years. Unfortunately, the Greeks took the most disastrous means possible to prevent this result and quickly became a degenerate (morally and spiritually) people; falling from a high degree of culture to little more than a memory. Our modern world is rapidly following in its footsteps.

[3] This development in itself is the proof of the degeneration and the gradual decay of the Greek race. There is only one *naturalness* native to the human creature and that is cohabitation as intended AND ARRANGED FOR BY NATURE. Any deviation, irrespective of the reason, is in the *direction of moral decay*.

Wherever there are actual needs for the limitation of children, there are natural, non-harmful means which in no wise bring about deterioration of morality or spirituality.

[4] A wholly misleading statement. It may be true, insofar as reproduction is concerned, but other serious consequences were then, as now, multitudinous; among them, first: moral debasement, animality, degeneration and, finally, mental deterioration and race suicide.

"So far as we can tell, neither the strength of the Greek race nor the standards of its culture suffered. Rather, they established a golden age which successive generations have tried to emulate—but not in their frank approach to sex."

We suggest that our readers study these several paragraphs carefully and in doing so, ask themselves the questions: Where is Sappho and her cult? Where is this mighty Greek nation and her standards of culture? Is this author suggesting that we follow the practices of the Greeks? Lastly, if it is true that neither the Greek race nor their standard of culture suffered, then why should the honest American worker and business man now be so heavily burdened by millions in taxes to defend, protect and feed this "strong and cultured nation" of a "golden age" from annihilation?

Tolstoi is remembered above all else for his command to the people: "Bethink yourself!" It were indeed well if the American people began in real earnest and sincerity to do so.

These SURVEYS and the commentaries have successfully accomplished one thing: something which the *verboten Le Kama Soutra* never succeeded in doing for the peoples of India, or even for the French people; a damage beyond repair; an evil that will continue as long as these texts are read.

It is an inborn instinct in the human creature, irrespective of how low he may fall, to hold on to something as an ideal; something as sacred. Hence the thief and the murderer, even the panderer, will think of his mother, sister or sweetheart as pure, noble and exalted.

The mother and father, irrespective of birth or culture, will think of their daughter as pure and undefiled; the youth will think equally well of his sister and sweetheart; the children of their parents; the girl of her lover. THIS USED TO BE TRUE, BUT IS TRUE NO LONGER.

Anyone, whether father, mother, youth or maiden, into whose hands these sex survey books unfortunately fall and who reads them, WILL BECOME INOCULATED WITH THE DEADLY POISON OF DOUBT; DOUBT THAT BECOMES SOUL SEARING AND DAMNING.

The youth meeting his sweetheart and looking into her eyes, innocent as they may be, will find the serpent doubt arising in his mind and wonder: "Is she, too, guilty of one or more of these practices? Is it true that she is no longer pure, no longer an ideal to be loved and worshipped?"

The lovely, innocent girl will be beset with these same damnable doubts when she greets her lover. The husband cannot help but think of them when he sees his wife. The wife will suspect the habits of her husband and mistrust every other woman.

Parents will doubt and suspect, if not mentally question the children, while the children in turn will doubt the purity of the lives of their parents. Each will suspect the other and never be able to entirely free the mind of suspicion.

If hell had opened its doors and spawned all its evils upon the face of the earth and its unfortunate inhabitants, no greater harm to man's ideals could have been accomplished than by the publication of these SURVEYS in the name of science and the conveyance of knowledge, with the resulting suspicions implanted in the minds of all who are so unfortunate as to read them.

Worst of all is the fact that no actual knowledge whatever has been gained by these SURVEYS. Mature mankind was well informed that these evils exist to some degree, but believed them limited to certain degenerate types. By these misleading SURVEYS they are now led to believe, or at least to suspect, that *almost all human beings,* beloved father, mother, brother, sister, sweetheart, husband and wife, *may be secretly guilty of one or more of these unsavory practices or vices.*

Moreover, all of the approaches are from the lower, animalistic, carnal plane, lacking all suggestion that there may be a higher, greater, spiritual concept, and a means for turning carnal thoughts, ideas and practices into avenues of idealism, exaltation and final spiritualization; or, as the Bible has it, the means of helping "mortality put on Immortality."

The approach is altogether wrong. It is an approach from the basest instinct in man; its concept is the gutter of human society. Men who have the welfare of the race at heart, who believe that a Regeneration of the race is possible and practical; men of the "cloth" of all churches, must gather together and give battle to this evil from the opposite direction.

It must be a spiritual approach; not one of smugness and self-righteousness, but an activity that is sane, practical, and, above all, HUMAN. It must be something that the common man who is honest, sincere, more or less moral, can understand and be able to accept; both the *reason* and the *modus operandi.*

The author of this book is positive in his condemnation of

all the evils of sex; the subterfuges employed to enjoy the creative act without assuming any responsibility. He believes that
sex is dual in its nature; reproductive on the one hand, REgenerative on the other; that it is human in reproduction; divine in
its possibility as an agent for REgeneration.

Life moves swiftly and not always constructively. Frequently
the efforts made to correct an evil, are more degrading and
destructive than the evil itself. This is most certainly true relative to affairs of sex.

After this text had been fully set into type, but before it
could be printed, the thinking world horrified by the news
emanating from Japan that that country had legalized Birth
Control.

It is admittedly true that Japan is desperately in need of
reducing its birth rate for the reason that the country is far
from able to supply the necessary food to its people; but the
method pursued should be in harmony with the Laws of both
Nature and of God — if it is possible to separate them.

If Japan legalized Birth Control clinics where the people
would be instructed in natural methods for the limitation of
childbirth it would be the proper thing, but the statesmen(?)
of Japan acted radically and legalized the establishment of what
will be neither more nor less than "Abortion rings," a crime
greater than the methods pursued in Greek when it was found
that the country could no longer adequately support its people.

The worst feature will be in the certainty that the lower,
irresponsible class, with few exceptions, will not take advantage
of the opportunities offered but will continue to breed as they
always have, while the better class, the responsible class will,

with the result that very shortly the "breeders," *not the leaders,* will be in control. It was so in Greece, it will be so in Japan.

With these thoughts in mind the work goes forth on its mission with the ardent prayer that it will be the means of destroying the suspicion that all men and women are guilty of sex evils. We also desire to awaken all who have the welfare of mankind at heart, to actively engage in teaching the truth, and nothing but the truth; the natural—and at the same time, the spiritual means—of meeting a difficult problem.

REV. R. SWINBURNE CLYMER, (M.D.)

Beverly Hall
Quakertown, Penna.
May 21, 1949

.

PROLOGUE

SANITY IN SEX IS SAINTLINESS IN LIFE

THE ETERNAL, CONSTANTLY ACTIVE LAW GOVERNING MAN AND ALL HIS ACTIVITIES MANIFEST AS A DUALITY AND A TRINITY

The DUALITY is found active in man's *two-fold* nature: His goodness, or God-like nature; and his evilness, or Devil-like nature. This is man as *he is; constantly at war within himself.*

The TRINITY is attained when man has learned to KNOW HIMSELF, as the ancients commanded. This means that man must come to understand himself; his weaknesses and evil inclinations on the one hand, and his strength or God-like qualities on the other.

He must finally succeed in *balancing the two;* rendering unto Caesar that which belongs to Caesar, and unto God that which belongs to God, denying or defrauding neither one nor the other. Such a man we say has attained to a form of deification; that is, he has become a Son of God.

There is no intention on our part to here write a treatise on religion, Spirituality or Godliness. Our interest for the moment is sex and the possibility of Race REgeneration by means of the "lifting up of the serpent" which is sex from the slime to which it was condemned by ignorance and the *tabu* of the church, and to call vivid attention to the uncontradictable fact, THE LAW, that as man is governed by a Duality and a Trinity,

SO IS SEX.

To deny sex or to hide it is to *suppress* it. This must always result in some form of DEgeneration of either mind, body and Soul, the spiritual part of man, or ALL THREE OF THEM. To more or less deify sex is to IMmortalize it. As a suppression of sex brings about some form of DEgeneration, we must consider sex and deal with sex as we must with the whole man.

We must recognize its proper function; its necessity to the continuation of the race as well as its application in the spiritualization of the whole man. In other words, we must neither deny nor deify sex, BUT MUST TAKE THE MIDDLE COURSE, completing the Trinity, and give sex its rightful, proper, sane place in life.

It is unreasonable to assume that man can think of God, love God, become *conscious* of God and at the same time ignore or suppress sex—the means of creation. It is equally unreasonable to consider sex as being *all of life;* giving it precedence in one's thoughts, desires and efforts. The one is as irrational and as abnormal as the other. Both lead to weakness and worse.

The middle course is the only rational, sane course to pursue. God did not give sex to man to ignore or to merely "multiplenish the race." Neither did he give man other things for one purpose only. Duality governs in all activity and the fullness of life is to bring this duality into a trinity of action.

The proof that sex and God are linked together, sacrilegious as this may at first thought appear, is found in the fact that the man or woman who has so abused sex as to have destroyed its very existence, is no longer capable of loving either the opposite sex or God. On the contrary, whoever is possessed of an abundance of sex ability or capacity, well controlled, is not only capable of the greatest love, but also possessed of the greatest ability to accomplish mighty works.

One of the evils, and there are many, is related neither to the sex nor the consciousness of its possession, but in *deifying* it; that is, in placing it upon a throne above all other things. "Thou shalt have no other Gods before me" is the command; this "no other" refers to all things man may desire, possess, make use of or abuse; not referring to sex alone.

It is almost as easy for a man to make "a god" of woman, of gold, or power, or of position, as it is of sex. Why, then, take the position that the evils growing out of sex are so much greater than the evils attributed to other things? All things that man can use or abuse are under the *one* Law.

For the married to engage in the marital embrace under the delusion that it is a sin, with a feeling of shame while under the compulsion of normal desire, IS A DEGRADATION NOT ALONE TO THOSE SO ENGAGED, BUT IS ALSO SACRILEGIOUS TO GOD, *as much as if man engaged in prayer with a sense of shame.* Both are holy and sanctified if the intent and the procedure are correct.

Just so long as man is led to believe and made conscious that the creative act is sinful and something to be ashamed of, just so long will he be unable to form a true concept of the God who created man with sex desire.

There is no law in heaven or earth which is one-sided or lop-sided. The Law is duality, hence that which is applicable to materiality, is likewise applicable to spirituality. In the fulfill-ment of this dual action of the Law will be found the *means* to Race REgeneration.

Let us not lose sight of the fact that the Infinite begins in the finite. Without the finite there could be no Infinite, at least in so far as man is concerned. The wise Creator recog-nized this fact in the creation of a body, moulded out of common earth, wherein to house the Soul which should sooner or later become Immortalized.

Here we have an example above all others that the Infinite must make use of the finite for its manifestation: an Immortalizable Soul imbedded in a body of clay. However, when man attempts to find selfish or complete satisfaction in the material and physical by means of *carnal* practices, then he is entirely on the wrong path.

The satisfaction of the physical and material may be based on what, under general conditions, would be carnal, but with a spiritual desire. Then the spiritual takes the place of the material, PROVIDED THE PROCEDURE IS CORRECT.

Does man not use material mind and heart during his prayers to God? And though his prayers proceed from man's material self, are they not acceptable to God? Is the creative organism less holy in the sight of God than mind and heart? If not, where then is the evil in the use of one and not the other, IF THE DESIRE, *i.e.,* THE INCENTIVE IS IN LOVE AND DEVOTION? God is not a respector of persons, hence He cannot possibly be a respector of the parts of a person, and remain GOD.

Two glaring misconceptions have enthralled the minds of men, lo, these many centuries. First: That man is possessed of an Immortal Soul; Second: That man seeks Infinite Love through the medium of finite beings.

These two illogical conclusions proceed hand in hand; neither one has a basis of fact. Man does possess a Soul; or, more correctly, the nucleus or *Spark* of a Soul; but, unless the Nazarene was very much in error, that SOUL IS NOT IMMORTAL UNTIL MAN HAS MADE IT SO BY MEANS OF REGENERATION, *i.e.,* THE SECOND BIRTH.

Secondly, the wise man does NOT seek Infinite Love by means of, or through the help of finite beings; what he does do if he is a normal man, is to *express* his Love for BOTH GOD AND THE SECOND HALF OF HIS BEING, HIS MATE, BY MEANS OF A FINITE ACT. The Love and worship of His God is one thing; the love for his mate is another side of his being.

The two in conjunction complete both his being and his worship; one does not interfere with the other, they complement each other; moreover, and what is of the utmost importance, is the indisputable fact that, unless God fostered a fraud upon his children, WHEN MAN ENGAGES WOMAN IN LOVE, HENCE IN WORSHIP, HE THEREBY NOT ONLY COMPLETES A SACRED RITE BY MEANS OF MUTUAL EXCHANGE, BUT HE LIKEWISE WORSHIPS GOD AND, IF THE ACT IS AS IT SHOULD BE, IT IS A MEANS OF REGENERATION; THE LIFTING UP OF THE SERPENT, HENCE OF THE TWAIN, TOWARD GOD.

If man engages in the act for purely self-satisfaction in order to relieve his lusts, then God and all His goodness will be left out of it, but if he follows the Divine Law, then Love is at the foundation of the act; LOVE GLORIFIED, and since GOD IS LOVE, AN ACT OF LOVE CAN NEITHER DEBASE MAN NOR LEAVE GOD OUT OF IT.

The creative act, as some ignorantly maintain, is NEVER followed by weakness, by a feeling of degradation, an aversion toward one's partner or a repugnance, BUT BY A FEELING OF EXALTATION, OF UPLIFTMENT AND OF GREATER LOVE. Only when self and lust prompt the act do these undesirable feelings follow in its wake.

The normal act of love—not mere satisfaction of a biological urge, though this is the unconscious part of it—does not *ever* permit man a feeling of escape from his responsibilities

to mankind and God, but instead, IT ADDS A FEELING OF
GREATER RESPONSIBILITY DUE TO THE KNOWLEDGE THAT
HAVING ACCEPTED THE "FAVOR" HE IS NOW BOUND TO
PROTECT THE PARTICIPANT IN THE RITE, FOLLOW WHAT
MAY.

The creative act, properly and holily engaged in, lifts man
from the lowly creature, first to *manhood,* and finally to
Godhood. He awakens his consciousness to a fixed certainty
that he is not merely a creature of God, but a co-creator with
God, and that if he desires to maintain the newly born MAN-
HOOD, he must not commit any mean or degrading act.

Guilt *never* follows in the wake of the marital rite if Love
is the base; if consent is won; if the act is normal, natural
and complete; the mutual exchange completed and the thoughts
turned toward Love and God.

Love is not license; not even liberty; LOVE IS AN ACT
WITHIN THE LAW and NEVER AN EVASION OR INFRACTION
OF THE LAW. Immorality is first a liberty taken, then a license,
and is followed by anarchy.

This is not possible where man is conscious of a proper
concept of God and His Divine Law. It is so only when men
have lost all faith in the existence of God due to a false and
misleading interpretation of His Laws.

Once the truth of the *possibility* of Immortality is fully
recognized, not as a free gift from God, but as something
man MUST EARN FOR HIMSELF BY THE ELEVATION OF HIS
THOUGHTS AND DESIRES, AND THE PURITY OF HIS ACTS,
MAN WILL NO LONGER DEGRADE ANYTHING, BUT WILL
STRIVE TO UPLIFT ALL HE CONTACTS. THIS INCLUDES HIS
SEXUAL BEHAVIOR MORE THAN ANYTHING ELSE, BECAUSE
IN THIS HE IS NOT ALONE, BUT ENGAGED WITH THE ONE

WHO POSSESSES HIS AFFECTION AND HIS LOVE, AS GOD
POSSESSES IT IN THE HEAVENS.

His acts begin in the finite, the temporal, and have their
reaction in the INFINITE AND ETERNAL. His Self-Love is
changed into love for another. His life is fused with that other;
moreover he feels eternally responsible for that other so long
as love lasts.

If sex were an evil in itself; if the exercise of sex were in
itself degrading, then it would most certainly be true that even
if engaged in for the sole purpose of propagation it would
be a sin.

If the engagement of sex is not a sin when so engaged,
then it follows that if Love is the base of the act, and if the
thoughts and desires of the heart be turned to God, it becomes
not only an act of creation, but also of worship, hence a Divine
Act and a DIVINE ACT IS A MEANS OF REGENERATION OR
REBIRTH.

Moreover, if the act is engaged in for creation it is not a
sin, and if conception does *not* follow, WHAT THEN? Is it
a sin? If it is, then who can FORETELL whether such an act
would be fruitful? If none can, and it is certainly true that
NO ONE CAN, then, in order to be on the safe side THREE
THINGS ARE ESSENTIAL:

First: The basis of the act must be Love and mutual consent.
Second: The possibility of pregnancy must be accepted.
Third: Because of the possibility that pregnancy may follow,
the act itself should be one of Love; with a desire to lift that
Love to God, and at the same time exchange the forces for
the upliftment, mentally, physically and spiritually, for the
benefit of those engaged in the act.

These three Laws obeyed, *and they are Laws,* sin does not follow the act and the result will be constructive and exalting.

The present cycle of immorality and unmorality in sex so rampant throughout the world is mostly due to a moral degeneracy in the individual and a consequent lack of faith in his fellow man.

By this we do not mean a moral degeneracy as concerns sex alone, but in its relation to true MANHOOD and PERSONAL RESPONSIBILITY.

To illustrate this it is necessary to refer to the first *open,* universal exemplification of this loss of MANHOOD AND PERSONAL RESPONSIBILITY—the *"scrap of paper"* incident of the first world war. Quickly following in the wake of the repudiation of his sacred word embodied in contracts, treaties, etc., by the Kaiser, other men in high position, authority and power followed his example and no longer was the word of a man recognized by, or acceptable to, his fellow man.

The man "whose word was as good as his bond" ceased to exist to all intent and purpose. This degeneration of the MORALITY OF MANHOOD BROUGHT ON A DISREGARD OF PERSONAL RESPONSIBILITY, AND THE DESTRUCTION OF THE DEEPER INNER RESPECT FOR ONE'S WORD OF HONOR— (A MAN'S WORD OF HONOR BEING SUPPOSEDLY HIS MOST SACRED POSSESSION ASIDE FROM HIS DEEP FAITH IN GOD)— AND THE DISREGARD FOR THE NECESSITY OF UPHOLDING PROPERTY RIGHTS QUICKLY FOLLOWED.

With the loss of personal honor, manhood, the appreciation of the sacredness and *inviolability* of one's *word of honor* and loss of respect for the sacredness of property rights, it was BOTH NATURAL AND INEVITABLE THAT WOMAN SHOULD QUICKLY LOSE HER INNER CONSCIOUSNESS OF HER VIRTUES.

IT WAS ALSO NATURAL THAT MAN IN TURN SHOULD CON-
SIDER HAVING AS MUCH RIGHT AND AS GREAT A LIBERTY
TO VIOLATE WOMAN'S SANCTITY, AS HE HAD TO VIOLATE
HIS NEIGHBOR'S PROPERTY. HE CONSIDERED THAT HIS WORD
OF HONOR SHOULD SERVE ONLY TO GAIN POSSESSION OF
WHATEVER HE DESIRED, IN ANY MANNER POSSIBLE, AND
THIS COULD BE QUICKLY REPUDIATED WHEN IT NO LONGER
SERVED HIM.

This lack of honor, of spiritual morality and personal
responsibility, has continually gained momentum. At this
moment the heads of State, the representatives of the people
and most of those in authority make treaties and give promises
today with little or no thought, ONLY TO REPUDIATE OR
CHANGE THEM TOMORROW. As a consequence, the people
as a whole no longer have faith in their representatives and
leaders and with this loss of faith in their chosen leaders, they
have lost faith in themselves as well as in God.

*And the basis of all this? The misinterpretation of the Laws
of God;* the instilling in the minds of men throughout the
centuries, that they may commit any crime under the sun;
any evil the mind can conceive and quickly be freed from all
responsibility—NOT BY A PAYMENT TO THE UTTERMOST
FARTHING, BUT BY A MERE REPENTANCE—A MERE "I am
sorry," and all will be well with them.

In the minds of men there has been a gradual but continually
growing suspicion of any Law, moral or spiritual, which would
forgive the gross transgressor—even if it be themselves—yet
hold their victims responsible for the sins caused by such trans-
gressions, if these victims failed to ask for such forgiveness.

Despite the loss of morality, the loss of the sense of honor
and lack of personal responsibility, the minds of men have

been slowly developing a consciousness of rightness and justice. This growing consciousness cannot conceive that a man can create a debt, no matter what its nature, and become free from it without he himself paying the full account.

This new concept is recognized as being at variance with all the inculcations of religion he has received, hence his loss of faith in religion and in God; he as yet is not able to differentiate between what is taught as religion, and THE ACTUAL LAWS OF GOD.

Loss of faith in religion, or perhaps more properly, the church, is apparent by a steadily growing lack of attendance at church services. The loss of confidence in his fellow men has left man with nothing to believe in, with the result that he has lost his spiritual anchor and has placed his trust in the things he can see and feel; the pleasures and profits of the moment.

Accepting this as true and long since having learned that the most certain means for his highest sense of gratification is found in sex, he has, to a large extent, made sex his god, *but without respect for the altar at which he serves.*

What else can he do? Because of the manner in which religion was served to him he no longer has respect for it. He has confused religion as he understands it, with God, hence has no respect for God. The men he knows are as sinful, as unreliable, unpredictable and undependable as himself, therefore he is unable to place either trust or reliance in them.

All that is left to him is his sense gratification; worship at the fount he knows will please and soothe, at least for a time. The sex-god is his only god. It at least is ever-present, never failing; the penalty is ignored, just as men ignore the ultimate penalty for their broken promises.

Man's concepts must be changed. The interpretation of Spiritual or Divine Laws must be reversed in such a manner that men who are still honest at heart will be able to respect the God who made them or gave them life. Man must be made conscious of the duality of his being.

Man must become cognizant that there is a material and a spiritual man; that the material man has rights and privileges, but that the spiritual man must also be satisfied. He must be made conscious that he is a personally responsible being; held so by the Law and will be forced to pay to the "last farthing," for any guilty infraction of the Law.

Once comprehending this, he will have respect for the Law because it is a *just* Law, and he will feel a newborn respect and reverence for the Giver of that Law.

Greatest of all is the need for men to come into the consciousness that there is a LAW OF SUBSTITUTION; a means and method whereby they may be compensated, or compensate themselves, for something needed or desired, by accepting another thing if the thing desired is not to be obtained.

Furthermore, part of this Law of *substitution* is the Law of *exchange.* Understanding this Law fully, men will select the things good for themselves because there is no penalty attached. If that is not to be had by command or selection, THEY WILL NOT DISHONOR THEMSELVES BY TAKING FOR THEMSELVES THAT WHICH DOES NOT BELONG TO THEM OR TO WHICH THEY HAVE NO RIGHT, BUT WILL EXCHANGE SOMETHING THEY DO POSSESS FOR SOMETHING THEY NEED OR DESIRE.

Once this is fully understood men and women will respect all they possess, will not take advantage of each other, dishonor or debase themselves, but instead, will honestly deal with each other; to the benefit of those concerned, and with loss or disadvantage to none.

Despite all appearances, it is fortunately *not* true as so many fearfully believe, that in the present cycle of civilization sex is debased as in no other age. History, both sacred and profane, records greater and more universal immorality than at present.

Though, during these periods, sex practices were indulged in to the degradation of all concerned, no one appeared to have the slightest concept that there may be a holy, a spiritual side to it; the nature of all things being in duality.

While the masses of today are guilty of gross degradation and immoralities, and honor has fallen low, it is nevertheless true that there is an ever-increasing number of both men and women who are becoming conscious of the real meaning of sex.

These recognize its correct and holy use and that, as it is the means of generation, it is also of equal potency in the REgeneration of both the individual and the Race.

Once this concept gains momentum, the pendulum will swing to the right, as it is now to the left. A new cycle of morality, sanctifying *manhood and personal responsibility,* as well as a new and greater faith in God and in Laws that are just and fair to all, will have its beginning. It is then when both sex (Caesar), and the spiritual side of man, the Soul (God), will receive proper and rightful consideration.

Men who have lost faith in God, hence in all *Law,* naturally, gradually and unconsciously become unrestrained. Since there is no law to obey, hence no threatened penalty, why not enjoy life to the full, and what better medium is there than in the *semblance* of love? Men either have a sense of honor, or they do not. Even honor is based on Law.

Where there is no law, self-interest governs. Teach men both by precept *and example* that there is a God, and that there are the *Laws of God* WHICH PERMIT NO INFRACTION, and men will begin to respect both God and His Laws, and as they gain respect, they will begin to obey the Law.

Teach men that while sex may be debased and degraded, there being a mortal and lower side, there is also a holy, sanctified, spiritual side based on *real* love and affection.

Just as the lowness of sex can and does debase, degenerate and destroy, so does exalted sex *lift up,* give greater life, deeper peace of mind and finally consciousness of God, *vide* the experience and example of Moses and his children in the wilderness.

In all honesty, whether one is priest or layman, it is unfair to expect any man to respect sex, sanctify and exalt it, when he is taught that sex in itself is evil; a necessary evil for the continuance of the race, but aside from that, something to be shunned, hidden in a dark closet and to be ashamed of.

It is equally erroneous to teach man either from a religious or a moral basis that passion in itself is a sin; a means to the degradation of man. So long as man is man he will be a passionate creature; if he is not, THEN HE SHOULD BE, *for otherwise he is a weakling and of little value either to himself or his fellow men, yea, even to God. Passion is a great force, a driving power, an incentive to action.*

There is no evil in passion; the evil is found in the manner of its direction; whether or not it is under the control of reason. The passionless man cannot love either his sweetheart, his wife, or his God. The sin is not in the possession of passion, but in its unwise direction; in its abuse; hence it is an error to believe that passion is an evil; that it is to be rooted out or destroyed.

In this as in all of life, RIGHT use, not abuse or destruction, is the Law; both religion and sociology should teach it. Man has too long been governed and mis-led by erroneous inculcations; all to his demoralization or destruction.

The comparison of man to animal in relation to sex is erroneous and degrading. The animal is governed by instinct and a rigid law of nature. In sex it obeys a biological urge. It does not reason; it does not think; it is merely true to its nature.

Man is, as so often mentioned, a dual being; a trinity in unity. He is a grossly material being, but he also has the capacity to become a highly spiritualized being. Like the animal, he is sexed. Unlike the animal, he has reason; he has feeling; he *is* passion. He has the privilege of being *governed* by passion; to permit his passion to stultify reason, and to degrade him.

On the other hand, he is able to govern and control his passion; to direct it by reason into the path of love which is affection, and through this love and affection, LIFT UP his passion to God, and with it LIFT up his mate.

Also, and at the same time, through the exercise of his passion by means of the marital rite, he may at once call into existence a new being; exchange forces with his mate for mutual benefit, *lift up* those forces by love to the REgeneration of their beings: hence their Souls to God.

It is all a matter of knowledge, of enLIGHTenment, and of the method pursued. The *means* are the same: sex and passion; the result is determined by the direction of its use. Sex for passion and self-satisfaction without love, is degrading; finally destructive; always dishonorable.

Sex *lifted up* upon the altar of love in holy desire, with recognition of its Holiness and sanctity, raises man and woman toward Godhood. Deny this, and you accuse God of a gross injustice to His creation; a diabolical intent in giving man a dangerous weapon which is destructive, lacking a means for his protection.

Sex is, at one and the same time, the lever that may lift man up to God, or degrade him, and sink him to the lowest hell. It is NOT sex that is to blame, but its misdirection; its abuse either wilfully or ignorantly. Love *under* the Law, IS THE LAW.

The church, *not* Christianity, consciously or unconsciously has been grossly guilty of inculcating the idea that sex is something to be ashamed of; either to be ignored, hidden or repressed, and in not teaching its followers the correct application of a mighty, world-governing force.

Furthermore, the church has ignored the teachings of the Law in relation to abuses, especially of the unholiness of the practice of pollution, the deadly results, hence, "sin" of the Biblically condemned practice of "casting the seed upon the ground," and worst of all, the three-fold purpose of what might well be termed the Holiness of *marriage* — the *Wholeness* of the embrace in its three-fold aspect.

The true union or exemplification of love and affection; the procreation of the race, and finally, the SPIRITUALIZATION of those who naturally engage in the marital embrace as intended by *both* nature and God, are all under the Law.

It is the duty of the church to teach these things. No other agency has this two-fold duty to perform; nor is any other agency justified by tradition to do so. This is a *holy* duty; a *divine* duty, therefore the work of the church.

The church, as well as some well-meaning but wholly uninformed reformers, may say that man's first duty is to God and that sex—speaking of sex as it should be naturally and normally—is secondary. This may appear to be correct at first thought—but let's look at another phase of the matter:

Man is born in ignorance. His actions are governed by instinct or "urges," until intuition takes the place of instinct, and wisdom the place of ignorance; but wisdom is attained only by experience.

This being accepted as true, the sex instinct, or biological urge, which contains within itself the desire for self-satisfaction, relief if you wish, is man's first and strongest desire.

Between the time of birth and the wakening of sex instinct, the child and youth may be instructed in law and order; in religion and his duty to God and his fellow man, but all this instruction, though accepted, IS NOT FELT, DOES NOT REALLY BECOME PART OF THE CHILD.

The first REAL *feeling,* aside from its love for parents, is when the awakening of sex takes place. It is in PREPARATION FOR THIS VERY THING THAT THE CHILD SHOULD BE WELL INSTRUCTED IN THE FUNDAMENTALS OF BOTH RELIGION AND THE REALITIES OF LIFE, SO AS TO BE FULLY PREPARED FOR HIS DUTY AS AN ADULT.

When the period of childhood gives way to manhood and womanhood, he or she will have the FAITH OF RELIGION TO LEAN UPON WHEN THE URGE OR DESIRE OF SEX BECOMES PRONOUNCED, AND BY THIS FAITH, WILL BE GUIDED, PERHAPS PROTECTED.

The wholly erroneous and misleading concept that repression or depression of an unlawful impulse as related to sex expression is less harmful physically and mentally than unlicensed or unhallowed expression, is no longer tenable.

If sex "urge" were merely a "desire" which might be brushed aside as are the many other desires which assail man during life, this might be true. But sex is NOT merely an impulse in the strong, normal, healthy man. It becomes an all-pervading urge; an almost unconquerable desire; a COMMAND BY NATURE FOR ITS EXERCISE. What is the remedy? *In Nature, its exercise should be in a normal, natural manner.*

That answer in itself is easy, but what if man is not so situated as to give sex natural expression under the laws of marriage? The answer is equally easy and the results will be the same, BUT THE PRACTICE IS ADMITTEDLY DIFFICULT: *Substitution.*

The youth must be taught ways and means to direct his life forces to the enrichment of mind, body and Soul through various activities: exercises, games, sports, recreation and all that helps to build a healthy body. Man and youth are governed by the same laws. It is right here where the Spiritual concepts are so all-important that man and youth may have the strength to withstand the tempter.

It is NOT true that repression as ordinarily known is less harmful than expression, even if this be unlawful—from the ethical-moral standpoint. Repression dams up the forces. It sets up congestion. It produces inflammations and affects both men and women.

Unlawful, that is, unnatural expression has the same effect but in a different manner. Too long have we taught what we *like* to believe and have misled mankind. We must now face

facts and teach the truth even though these truths are not altogether to our liking.

Man's *true* mission on earth is to GLORIFY GOD AND BECOME
LIKE HIM. That implies bringing into manifestation and activity
all of his potentialities. On the one hand this implies becoming
a procreator with God, and this is possible by means of generation, in which sex is fundamentally involved. This is number
one on man's agenda.

Next to this, in fact completely interwoven with it, is God's
command to man to Love, and in love, to be like Him. In God-
ordained generation, *love and affection between those engaged
in sex embrace must have as great a part as does the desire of
sex and its ultimate satisfactory ending.*

Here again God is made a part, a co-creator. To speak of
God in this connection may appear sacrilegious to prudes and
weaklings, but not to the manly MAN who is capable of both:
sex in its fullness and love-affection.

Last is the almost pure—there is nothing wholly pure where
mortal man is concerned—Spiritual concept, which turns the
thoughts and desires of the most inward being, toward God and
all that is holy, during the marital—Love—embrace; thoughts
of worship of God rather than the desire for satisfaction.

We can here well quote a Biblical statement from *St. John*
6:60: "This is an hard saying, can ye understand it?" and answer
by saying that none are capable of understanding it except
THOSE WHO TRULY AND FULLY LOVE.

In order to be capable of GLORIFYING GOD it is essential that
there be active, deep within us, a desire to attain to the highest;
which naturally implies becoming perfect. *No man can or will*

ever be able to attain to perfection unless he uses all of his abilities and potentialities to the full and in the manner intended.

Sex being the very foundation, the very beginning of his existence, it implies that his creative ability must be exercised as well as his constructive knowledge, all in a natural, normal manner, but *exercised they must be.*

This again implies the "self." But this self must not be confused with selfishness. *Every* man is born for the purpose of improving himself and to that end is given every opportunity to not merely help himself but to develop himself in every manner possible.

It is his FIRST DUTY to help—HIMSELF, before he even attempts to help other men—humanity. By learning to help himself he gains the knowledge with which to teach others to help themselves; helping himself, therefore, is a double duty.

If he can be made proud of himself and his capabilities, then like the good husbandman, he will carefully and sacredly guard everything, every means of value in his quest for perfection. He will abuse or misuse nothing. All that he is, all that he possesses, will be turned to good account; THIS INCLUDES SEX.

To come to the crux of the matter, no Christian, using the term in its *esoteric* sense as *meaning one who has become conscious of the Christos* or Christic Spirit within himself, will be guilty of sex abuses or the abnormalities associated therewith. Why not? Because to do so means self-pollution and self-pollution means a degradation of that Christic Spirit within.

If, and when, the church teaches the exact sex laws—teaches them truthfully and fearlessly—that of the many degrading practices now rife among society, one of the most degrading and destructive is *Conjugal fraud* in one form or another, *i.e.,* the Biblical "casting of the seeds upon the ground," and the punishment in the form of ailments of the genital organs in the female and Prostatitis and other serious diseases in the male, a good beginning toward sex purity and self-upliftment will have been made.

Dare physicians and churchmen do this frankly, openly and unreservedly or will they continue to play with the *fire* that has destroyed nations and will continue to destroy them until men, through suffering, gain wisdom for themselves?

INSTRUCTIONS FOR GIRLS

F THE many who have soiled countless reams of paper dealing with this vastly important problem, few have dared to deal frankly and honestly with it and place the blame where it rightly belongs.

How many millions of parents in the past have asked the questions: "Why do girls allow themselves to be led astray?" and: "Why do our girls, apparently deliberately, choose the wrong path? Surely, they must know the difference between right and wrong; between the status of the 'kept' woman and the maiden who has remained unsullied?"

Roughly, we would classify the causes as follows:

1. A love of ease that is stronger than virtue or morality.

2. Love of pleasure that is greater than the desire for purity and respectability.

3. The love of ease and position greater than the respect for public opinion.

4. A love of possession stronger than any other desire.

In all these instances the desire for the things sought after is greater and deeper than the longing for affection and to be loved for the self alone. Little or nothing can be done to prevent any one of these from following her natural inclination. Only misfortune, deep sorrow or great suffering will lead one so insensible of virtue from the left-handed to the right-handed path.

The other classes — and these greatly outnumber the first four mentioned — can be roughly divided into:

1. Those who fall into error because they love and are led astray by the promise of love and its legitimate fulfilment. These fall as a result of faith and trust. They are virtuous and clean of heart; though they are betrayed, they are not "fallen" women; never will be, because the love which caused them to be misled and then failed them, will be turned into love for their progeny.

The universal formula, varying but little, of those who have misled them and will mislead millions yet unborn, is: "If you love me you will do as I request; if you will not, then I know you do not love me."

Since it is a universal law that women sacrifice for love, it is a foregone conclusion that they will comply and, if the lover is without honor, one more will be added to the great army of those who have "loved," most probably innocently, but not wisely. In almost all instances, these women make good mothers and excellent wives for any man who will thereafter truly love them.

2. The last and perhaps most pitiful class is the great army of girls in homes where there is neither peace nor happiness; where they are given little attention and less encouragement. These are homes where no love is shown them; where they receive little or no instructions; where they are given no part in the family relationship.

They are not wanted, or if they are, there is no real indication of it. They are not made to feel they are an actual part of the family, or that they have any responsibility in the family life. On the contrary, they are made to feel that, at best they are little more than driftwood; tolerated until they can find someone to take them out of the family circle. They receive little or no affection from either father or mother and are constantly

accused of wrongs of which they are actually innocent and never
even dreamed of committing.

Longing for love and receiving none at home, they fall easy
victims to the first seemingly decent man who offers them
his sympathy. At heart they are as pure and clean as the
girls who listen to the voice: "I love you; if you love me,
you will do as I wish. PROVE IT."

In these cases, and they are legion, THE PARENTS ARE
WHOLLY TO BLAME. A little love, a little more understanding,
and they would have been safe from evil.

THE PARENTS OF TODAY, BOTH AS REGARDS BOYS AND
GIRLS, ARE MOST OFTEN THE CAUSE OF JUVENILE WRONG-
DOING. THEY FAIL IN FURNISHING A REAL HOME LIFE
TO GROWING BOYS AND GIRLS—A HOME WHERE THERE IS
LOVE, AFFECTION AND MUTUAL UNDERSTANDING. THESE
HUMAN DESIRES ARE THEREFORE SOUGHT ELSEWHERE AND
THE PRICE PAID IS FEARFUL. IT IS THE PARENTS WHO IN
MOST INSTANCES ARE GUILTY OF JUVENILE DELINQUENCY:
THE PARENTS WHO SHOULD BE MADE TO PAY.

It seldom occurs to the millions of questioners and reformers
that if the average girl were given a correct understanding of
herself, proper instructions and training, plus sympathetic
understanding, therein would be provided the most certain preventive of making a wrong choice.

If a girl actually has an understanding and appreciation of
the source and meaning of the sex impulse, *the nature of the
desire,* the incentive to mate or be loved, she will be prepared
to protect herself and at the same time retain the affection
of the man who expresses a love for her. She will KNOW
that to refuse improper requests is to become doubly desirable.

Unquestionably the mothers of exceptional character and broadmindedness, possessed of love for their offspring and with the right attitude, who would instruct their daughters correctly if they knew how, are almost uncountable. It is their heart's desire that their girls shall remain virtuous and innocent of wrong, but they are at a loss to know how to properly guide them.

Evil itself is relative: the results of error are positive. It must be recognized that there are many and varying degrees of so-called "fallen" women. A girl may go astray; yet be truly virtuous in heart and Soul, and following her "fall" may continue in virtue, or become bitter and a woman of ill-repute. The direction of her action will depend entirely upon her disposition, her environments and the understanding of those around her.

The primary motive and cause must always enter into consideration and judgment of each individual case. Any number of girls, having made a mistake without evil intent, or led into making a mistake, recognize it for what it is, then proceed to reconstruct their lives and take their place in respectable society.

If the truth must be told, they are probably the better and more tolerant of others because of their unfortunate experience. Others again, for one reason or another, for which they may not be to blame, follow the downward path until disease, then friendly death, releases them from chains too strong to be broken.

Contrary to general opinion, there are conditions in the life of a woman more to be feared than the loss of innocence or first misstep, *i.e.,* secret, unnatural, morbid, Soul-destroying solitary vices more degrading than the sex embrace outside of matrimony. For those who momentarily ignore the moral code there is every hope of correction and a useful, constructive life.

The girl who becomes habituated to unnatural inclinations and practices is seldom capable of becoming a satisfactory, satisfied wife and mother; the moral fibre itself having undergone a form of disintegration, a recurrence of habit, degeneration and possibly finally some form of imbecility all too often follow.

Two special reasons have been advanced for the downfall of the majority of girls: (1) Love, or what passes as love, and want of love or affection; and (2) desire for money or the things money can buy.

Of the first class it is safe to say that fully eighty-five percent of all instances were due to this cause. We say *were* and refer to the past century; now there are many other reasons as already stated.

The second class we pass by because there is little that can be done for them unless their desires can be satisfied in some manner before they take the decisive step.

As the normal girl approaches womanhood, she becomes conscious of a desire *for* affection and an *outlet* for her own affection. She is fortunate, indeed, if she has parents who understand and act accordingly.

She is made aware of an awakening within herself of what will later become the mother instinct; a desire to *offer* herself to one who understands or who she believes will understand her. It is to be borne in mind at all times that normally women are far different from men in their outlook and feelings toward life in general.

Where the man seeks for self-satisfaction in almost all things, the woman seeks to *give,* and by giving, receive vicariously. Perhaps—who knows—the great religious leaders may have based the theory of VICARIOUS ATONEMENT on this normal and natural feminine instinct.

The true woman, more especially the young girl entering adolescence and the woman approaching motherhood, *deifies* the object of her affection, bestowing generously of her worship, endowing him or it with godlike qualities and is therefore the more easily persuaded that her love must be proved to the uttermost. Perhaps that is why she so readily falls—unconsciously reaching out for a way or means to prove her love — she is easily seduced and led astray. Her motive is pure; she is actuated by impulses as old as mankind, although this motive or urge, even today, is but dimly understood.

It is a truth that all too many natures are incapable of comprehending they are committing "sin" when their consent is won "for Love's sake." *If otherwise sane and sensible parents of young girls could be made to fully understand this secret, very few of our normal, natural, healthy girls would be led astray.*

Countless women possessed of highly (sensitive) organized nervous systems and of deeply religious nature, unconsciously deify their love consciousness by personifying it. Proof of such deifications and personifications are to be met with in all religious literature, a specific instance of which reference is to be found in *Gasgrain's* VIE DE MARIE L'INCARNATION.

This Marie of the confession is ready and willing to offer life itself that her desire for love, which she feels is divine, may be satisfied or fulfilled.

She confesses: "Going to prayer, I trembled and exclaimed, 'Let us go into a solitary place, my dear love, that I may embrace you, at my ease, and that, breathing my Soul into you, it may be but yourself only, in the union of love. Oh, my love, when shall I embrace you? Have you no pity on me in the torments that I suffer? Alas, alas, my love, my beauty, my life! instead of healing my pain, you take pleasure in it. Come, let me embrace you, and die in your sacred arms.' Then, as I was spent with fatigue, I was forced to say: 'My divine love, since you wish me to live, I pray you let me rest a little, that I may better serve you,' and I promised him that afterward I would suffer myself to consume in his chaste and divine embrace."

> Despite all that has been said and written by those who have had little or no experience in the psychology of love, hence no first-hand knowledge, this same inner desire for love and a means to give it expression, governs the motives and actions of normal healthy girls and women of tender age. It is the age-old Psyche and her complicated and much involved love, desire, biological urge and motherhood complex without which mankind would soon cease to exist.

We have personally received the confession of many women, highly respected in their communities, who, *destructively frigid in their sex relationship with their husbands,* would attend religious revival meetings, and, having their emotions aroused through the hectic, and often fanatic, sermons, and the expressed, verbal and by motion, emotions of the congregation, would *pass through the sensual-nervous crisis* as does the normal, healthy woman in embrace with her husband. Such a woman on her return home to her "lord and master," following the experience just described, would be as cold and virtuous (?) toward him, as ever.

However, in this department of our work we are dealing with the normal, healthy young woman who is capable of loving and desirous of being loved; not with the emotionalism of the hectic, fanatically religious, unbalanced-minded class.

Every mother is aware, if she has given the subject any thought whatever, that sex-awakening must come to her daughter, and that she, better than anyone else, is qualified, or should be qualified, to bring about such an awakening. She cannot fail to remember her own thoughts and desires during the days of her youth, and this remembrance should impress upon her that intimate sex knowledge is essential to the life of *every real woman.*

The gradual process of the development from innocent maidenhood to desired womanhood, with its unfoldment and possibilities must not be accepted as a condition to be suppressed, crushed, ignored, or apologized for.

It is neither unholy, nor unnatural; quite the opposite. No greater blessing was ever bestowed upon woman than this most holy and desirable emotion of seeking *to be possessed completely.* It is a divine, deific promise, given in advance, of her value to the race of real men; that through this sex impulse she may add to the sum total of human happiness; become a channel for the birth of superior creatures, thereby hastening her own evolution conversely, or she may bring misery to herself and her progeny, delaying her own progress toward perfection. The results are always in exact ratio to what she has been taught as the truth, and the extent of her cooperation in the effort.

Mothers dare no longer shrink from the positive duty they owe their daughters. The origin, nature and effect of sex emotion and indulgence must be fully, sanely, and elevatingly explained; evasion and innuendos are misleading and delusive. When the girl receives enlightenment on both the cause and effect of her emotions, she will possess the weapon which knowledge alone can give.

The fear that an open discussion over-reaches the desired results, that the young are induced by curiosity to investigate hidden paths after they have been instructed, is not a sane or logical argument. The subject denuded of its false, insidious, secret aspect, presented in a normal, unprejudiced manner, will do much to curb undue interest. The beautiful, desirable and constructive, as well as the hideous, damning and destructive phases, all must have consideration.

Knowledge may add intensity to the girl's nature, but innate goodness, fortified with understanding, will be an incentive for her to follow the right path. *Normal girls, as a whole, are naturally pure in thought and desire* and will not be led to ruin through knowledge. Ignorance alone is to be feared.

One manifestation of the feminine sex nature (often the direct cause of the girl's undoing) scarcely, if ever, is given the serious consideration it deserves. This is the *instinctive, inborn,* mother-love nature, the natural inheritance of *every* normal female.

The moment the true woman loves, at that instant does she begin to seek a means to serve. It is her innate nature inducing a longing in her to supply all the wants of the loved one, whether of a social, mental or physical nature.

His comfort and well-being become her aim in life, and if she be uninstructed, the whisperings of her conscience will scarcely be heard and certainly avail nothing as against his pleadings.

He appears restless and hungered and in order to appease him, she readily offers herself—an unconscious sacrifice. *The call of sex desire in her, though playing a part, is not as a rule the actual reason for her compliance with his request; it is the urge of the mother-love plus the desire to be possessed.*

The ideal wife is half mother to the object of her love; she serves her husband as though he were a child; grants all his favors, whether demanded in or out of season.

A thorough explanation of this infinitely varied and complex side of her nature must be offered the girl, thus guarding her against an unwise sacrifice on the altar of love.

The actual purposes and usage of her creative nature are not understood by one girl in a thousand; generally all the information the many possess was gained from unreliable sources; from companions as ignorant of the actual facts as they themselves.

Because of this undesirable condition, the great need to prevent the multitude of innocent girls being led astray into "love unions," or what *appear* as love-unions, blindfolded, is for sane, sensible, thorough instruction and training.

Girls are best reached through the mother; boys through the father. But fathers and mothers must first be taught the laws and powers, uses and abuses of sex. *Above all, the penalty resulting from disobeying these sex laws, either through ignorance or choice, must be fully inculcated.*

When fathers and mothers are imbued with the divinity of all of God's creation, no department of life will appear more sublime than this one through which He makes us co-creators with Him.

When they realize this sublimity and harmonize it with

knowledge, they are then in a position to outline the path that their young may follow in freedom and protection.

So long as parents possess only the sensational, crude, vulgar, and distorted conceptions of sex based on mis-information obtained during their own youth, so long as they believe this important subject is to be discussed in a veiled, obscure, secretive manner, ridiculed and condemned in public, just that long will they, *the parents, be blameworthy and held accountable by God and the moral law for the sins and the shame and the suffering of their progeny.*

Up to within a very short time ago it was a crime to teach anything that concerned sex and its expression. The time will soon come when men and women with families will be held responsible for the sex education and enlightenment of their sons and daughters, and it will be considered criminal if they neglect this sacred duty. Perhaps by then the church also will see the light and become active in the education and protection of the young in their charge.

What opinion would be formed of a man or woman who presented the boy or girl with a dangerous and intricate mechanism, compelling the child to make use of it, yet withholding knowledge of its operation and its dangers?

Suppose that machine combined both life-giving and death-dealing qualities, and the giver refused to offer any instructions for its operation and the protection of the person—would we not rightly feel abhorrence toward him and seek his incarceration?

As a further illustration, imagine this same parent keeping close guard over the helpless child, building an impassable wall of "parental authority" about it, menacing the competent men and women who were pleading for the privilege of instructing the child in the operation of the potent instrument. Is it not an appalling picture?

If the modern enlightened mother were informed that her daughter possessed some great talent, would she urge the girl to dedicate it to the devil, having been informed that sin, sickness, misery and death were the consequences? On the contrary, would she not rejoice and help develop the desirable gift, uplifting and praising it, thus bringing joy, power, health and beauty to the daughter she loved?

Would a father willingly allow his children to play with a viper? Would not the heart contract with horrible fear at the very thought of its fangs and poison?

Despite the conjured-up picture, innumerable careless or ignorant parents are brutally indifferent to even greater and ever-present dangers and close their eyes to plain, uncontradictable facts. They leave their children to the malignant influences of ignorance, more deadly than the fangs of the viper, for these can destroy the body only. When ignorance takes its toll, they bewail their fate and impeach the Father of all-good, blaming Him, instead of themselves, when a daughter enters the brothel instead of a home; becomes the mother of an unnamed child, or suffers a lingering death from some loathsome disease.

Who, at the great accounting, will be judged guilty, and suffer the greater punishment? Surely not the child born and raised in ignorance, lacking all knowledge of the evils confronting it, or how to protect itself.

The basis of sex instruction should be the *holiness of sex.* There is nothing degrading in normal passion. The only profane phase is the destructive thought of prejudiced, ignorant humanity, and the ignoble purpose to which sex is perverted as a natural result.

It is not enough to preach of the swift penalty following debasement of the creative function; the pure, exalted, sacred purpose must be enlarged upon. The possibilities for good or evil of the generative organism must be minutely taught; the dark, secret, and destructive usages of which humanity is guilty must be fully exposed.

Parents and teachers must search their own hearts for the slightest trace of impurity of thought; youth being psychically expert in sensing the least hint of shame, or the feeling of self-consciousness. Many who are today invaluable as teachers and leaders in the enlightening movement learned their lessons after reaching maturity, or through great personal suffering and the consequent adjustment, purification and self-effacement. All these, as with one voice, proclaim the necessity of purity of thought.

Of the many false conceptions respecting sex and its functions, that of repression is the most destructive and degrading. It has been impressed, more by inference than by actual words, that woman is coarse and unwomanly if she allows sex desires to become manifest. It has been taught that women, even if passionate, should not express their real feelings, but hold them in subjection, as something of which to be ashamed. Adherents to such beliefs become victims of the goddess of ignorance and gradually come to believe it unbecoming and even unrighteous to display any emotion during the marital rite.

In the marriage rite, woman has every right to as great an enjoyment as man. God gave passion equally to the male and the female; therefore the coldness resultant from restraint and of repression is unnatural. Under no circumstances should natural desires be denied and repressed and their possession considered with shame. Repression is the pathway to abnormal physical and emotional upsets; and if continued for any length of time, gives rise to degraded and perverted desire, followed by practices destructive to creative ability. Admittedly, passion should be held in proper subjection—wisely directed; this calls for the exercise of the Will.

Many males, incorrectly termed men, subscribe to the theory that women should repress their real feelings, then proceed to condemn them for being cold; these have not yet reached the degree of enlightenment where they are willing to grant equality; have not arrived at an understanding of the necessity of the normalcy and desirability of passion in women. These men still remain in bondage to the past and consider it immodest for women to meet them with sincere feeling; possessing a divine right for equal exchange.

Girls must be taught that normal, controlled sex power is forever creative if rightly used and not abused; that if the creative forces are diffused throughout the body, they become the basis of strength and beauty of body, and brilliancy of mind. The perfection of woman's form, the smoothness, loveliness and texture of her skin, the sweetness of her voice and the fire of her eyes all depend on, and are due to, this creative energy.

When the girl finally comprehends that every part of her nature is God's gift to her to be used according to His law, she will rejoice in her possessions and nothing will be able to tempt her to debase them, nor will she do ought that may cheapen herself in any manner.

She must be brought to an understanding that unnatural

repression, trying to root out, or kill any desire or function, is equally as wrong as misuse of that desire or function. Her sole duty is to be mistress of herself; to control the passions that at times rise and surge within her, until such time as she meets the right mate who will prove his love by contracting a partnership with her through holy wedlock.

Questions most frequently asked: "What are we to do with our daughters while they are passing the dividing line between girlhood and womanhood, possessed of an abundance of life, love, and creative instinct; how can we help them to control their desires?"

The first requisite is to keep the mind fully occupied with duties to be performed, or problems to be solved. So long as they are wholeheartedly interested in work and play, they are safe.

Treat the girls as we do the boys. Boys are active creatures and free themselves of excessive energy by work and athletics, recreation and special interests. Allow the girl to romp and be a tom-boy to her heart's content; you will never find the seed of sex trouble as long as she does this. When that age and stage is past, she must be induced to find interest in some other task or practice.

Work given her must be neither monotonous nor confining. Change is essential, as is time spent in the open air; and in whatever constructive activity she centers her mind she must be continually encouraged; it is imperative she have an *incentive* to act.

Above all, the home life must be made pleasant, her problems met with kindness, understanding and always with great patience.

Admittedly, not all girls can be guided in this manner. In the quiet, sedentary, studious, the pursuit most interesting to them should be encouraged; while the more active physical exercises should not be forced upon them. Music, painting, the arts, *whatever they can be interested in,* should be indulged, care being exercised that the fancy does not lead toward the morbid.

Interest is the key. Instruct the girl in the laws governing sex, then keep her interested and the entire problem finds a solution of itself. The moment a girl becomes dissatisfied, the danger signal quickly becomes apparent.

The duty of every mother is positive. She must as closely devote her attention to the development of her daughter as the father does to his business. A man pays careful attention to every detail of his vocation, studies continuously how to combat certain influences; how to remedy leakage and deficits; is eternally vigilant. The mother's daughter is *her* business, and she must apply herself in like manner. If all is not as it should be, *seek the cause;* make necessary changes; be deft in the art of substitution.

Far too frequently the normal, healthy, vivacious, active girl is deprived of necessary innocent pleasures. She wishes to visit a friend, attend the theatre, witness a game, go on a picnic, or attend a party. These innocent pastimes are refused her; she is *thrown back upon herself; trouble brews,* and a deplorable situation quickly develops.

Her mind becomes resentful; seeking an outlet for her dammed-up energy, she allows her imagination to play too freely, and if evil companions or blasé stories have previously opened the way, *the devil steps in.*

The average girl, at this stage of her development, is not expected to set aside all pleasure; noble, elevating thoughts alone will not sustain her at this period of her life. When pleasures are denied, solitary vice, or secret meetings with the undesirable of the opposite sex, are almost certain to follow.

The solution of the problem is found in:

1. Teaching the girl the creative laws in detail and frankness; presenting every side clearly, especially dwelling on all that is beautiful, fascinating, beneficial, and constructive to herself and the race.

Invite questions and reply without hesitation, in chaste language and without self-consciousness. Praise her (within reason) to assist her in a correct valuation of herself. *Be her friend and confidant* at all times and under all circumstances.

2. Supply her with work of an interesting nature. Dwell much on the honor of housekeeping and motherhood. Temporary employment about the house permits her to become efficient in housekeeping, or preliminary training for a vocation is highly desirable. Encourage the development of any apparent talent.

Do not allow her to become one-sided and impractical. Unless a girl has positive genius, it is better to encourage her to do several things well. The sensible, adaptable woman becomes the best wife and mother.

3. Exercise is one of the essentials. Any method, if constructive, is desirable. Games, tennis, rowing and walking are all highly important. If these do not suffice or appear unsuitable, arrange for regular gymnastic work. The object is to keep the body agile, the blood in active circulation, and the creative forces distributed.

4. Amusements are as important as exercise. All pleasure should combine harmless recreation with elevating tendencies. It is questionable whether any but the most esthetic girls could remain normal and free from vice without sufficient amusements.

Girls drift into the downward path because their requirements are neither recognized nor provided for by their natural guardians. Parents fail in their duty and this neglect cannot be corrected in after life.

During the formative period girls learn of matters concerning sex, and more often than not, it is the degrading conception that they acquire rather than an elevating comprehension of the influence and potency of the functions and forces. Once fully impressed with the wrong ideas, the girl becomes incapable of either understanding, or finding true love; consequently she is condemned to live on the husks of affection.

Parents generally seem to make but little effort to understand their daughters, their feelings, likes and dislikes, their inclinations, weaknesses and strength. They urge them to accomplish either too much or too little, allow them no amusements at all, or satiate their desires by overdoing. A sane, balanced, intelligent parent is a God-send, an angel of mercy, to any child. Let us hope for more such in the near future.

The girl of the present is an independent creature and it is unwise to either suspect her motives; accuse her of indiscretions, or to impute wrong to mere folly and inexperience. Parents should be absolutely certain of their information before even asking questions and *never* be guilty of making accusations. If there is guilt, meet it with understanding, sympathy and corrective instructions.

Mothers should love their daughters into obedience; counseling them rather than commanding them. The young, whether boys or girls, can more readily be loved than punished into goodness. Have faith in your children; trust them; be companions and good fellows with them; correct their mistakes, *then quickly proceed to forget them.* Share your sorrows with your children AND THIS WILL TEACH THEM TO FEEL. Share your joys, pleasures and good fortune with them; this will ASSURE THEM THAT THEY HAVE YOUR LOVE AND THAT YOU HAVE THEIR BENEFIT AT HEART. Be their parents, but also THEIR FRIENDS AND CONFIDANTS and you need have little fear that they will go astray. The child should be fully conscious of the fact that whatever its fault or guilt, it can approach the mother or dad in complete confidence of a kindly hearing without being subjected to a lecture and that the opinion offered will be unbiased and unprejudiced. Such a child will not make a confidant of strangers or those who might mislead him or her. WHATEVER THEY MAY BE GUILTY OF, BE A "GOOD FELLOW" TO YOUR CHILDREN. *You would be if they were your neighbor's children.*

THE PURITY OF SEX

To the Pure in Heart All Things Are Pure

THE same general proverbs, adages and axioms are found among all peoples, irrespective of the age, source or to whom addressed. Throughout the world there is a similarity in the recognition of moral truths. "Unto the pure all things are pure," has found its way through many holy books of the long past, and likewise appears in the Bible of our time. Men agree with this truism without hesitation until the subject of sex is introduced, then they retire in confusion — their senses benumbed by a consciousness of inner guilt.

In the animal kingdom, the law governing mating and reproduction is accepted as a matter of course. Men see nothing to be ashamed of in the breeding of animals. Selecting the participants, they watch and assist at the birth of the young; feed and train them; again selecting the future breeders; meanwhile enthusiastically discussing their good and weak points without a thought of either self-consciousness or concealment.

As a matter of fact, many men pride themselves on their success in producing superior stock; unconscious of any sense of shame when discussing the methods of breeding; the perpetuation of desirable traits; form or color, and the eradication of questionable qualities and kindred subjects common to thousands upon thousands of breeders of animals. Let the attention be turned to human reproduction, however, a subject of *infinitely* greater importance to both God and man—and what happens? Every one, almost without exception, will turn aside to hide their ignorance, prejudice or shame, with a display of supposedly righteous virtue.

Dr. J. H. Greer, formerly Professor in the College of Medicine and Surgery, Chicago, lecturing on the subject of sex, said: "Throughout the domain of nature the instinct of sex is paramount. In the highest kingdom of life the instinct is subject to the modification of civilization which, alas, is not always the best. The lives of all men are colored by the thoughts of sex, which may be of the varying shades between good and bad.

"Asceticism, on the one hand, strives to suppress as impure all thoughts and feelings regarding the relations of the sexes. Those who are so narrow as to conform to the letter while ignoring the spirit of true religion may be cited as the most baneful of combatants of pure thought on the subject.

"On the other hand is the unchaste, immoral sensualist, who believes that life means gratification of the senses, the most exquisite of which is the sexual relation. He drains the wine of life to the dregs, and, when at last sated, can see nothing of the true use of the bodily senses. These extremes exist because men do not know the truth."

We would dispel this murky cloud by assisting humanity to a knowledge of the *development of a superior* race; and, in the effort, avoid both extremes. There is a sane, middle course untinged by any cult or ism; one that we have, through long experience, found worthy of acceptance as a standard of life for all men.

This course adjusts sexual and physical inharmonies, bringing in its train health and happiness as the result of sane exercise of the Creative functions. Those who have attempted to find truth by following the false path of continence will be benefited equally with those who have pursued the opposite course: that of license and debauchery.

The constructive path lies *midway* between the two extremes and leads to the fountain of life; aye, the *Fountain of Youth* so much sought. Those who choose this course in life discover the beauty and divinity of sex and quickly recognize the Laws of God, controlling the functions, as just and righteous. Correctly understood, the truths concerning sex do not bring a blush to the most saintly cheek; nothing being discoverable in God's laws to humiliate, or mortify man; the sense of shame belonging *only to those who live life shamefully.*

Why should sex be considered impure? Can it be in itself degrading? *Only its abuse makes it so.* Of itself, it is pure, for *God made all things pure.* Why differentiate between humans and animals, giving the latter all that is best in thought and service, as respecting reproduction and the creating of a superior species, while discouraging and condemning all that concerns the like functions in man?

Is not a clean, virtuous, healthy woman God's greatest and most beautiful handiwork, a thousandfold the superior of any animal ever born? Why then is the human feminine degraded by man, and the animal female studied, petted, and developed, their duty and functions in the world of reproduction being exactly alike?

The answer is not far to seek: The mind and heart of the males, and many females (not *men and women),* have become so perverted, defiled, and unspeakably filthy from dwelling in lewd thought of contact, gratification and sensation, *that the spiritual side has never been recognized by them.*

The man who can find impurity in sex, who can think of it

with any thought but of God's loftiest intention, should undergo a long period of mental, physical and spiritual cleansing.

One is lost in the labyrinth of futile conjecture when attempting to find an answer for the foulness, ignorance and baseness of many of the human species, the subject of sex generally brings a knowing leer to the face, a licentious look to the eye, while unbridled thoughts manifest through the entire organism. Even good and virtuous women, at the mention of the creative function, cast down their eyes, give evasive answers, and hasten to shift the discussion to a less delicate subject.

What has brought humankind to such a mental state of impurity? In the beginning it was undoubtedly a lack of sex information and incomplete understanding of God's Creative function. In addition, there was also the actual and literal encouragement of degraded, perverted, vile and untruthful ideals.

Evil thrives in darkness or ignorance, and almost every mother in the world, good of heart as she may be, and unquestionably is, has been guilty of instilling in the mind and heart of children glaring untruths when first questioned on the subject of sex.

This is the seed or foundation responsible for all future falsehood concerning the reproduction of her kind. What a fearful indictment of mankind generally in an otherwise enlightened age.

It is often maintained that the world is spiritually and morally improving; but trust and blind faith are required to believe this assertion, when we are confronted with the various forms of license and debauchery rampant in the great cities of today. The history of *Sodom* and *Gomorrha,* destroyed by fire because of the unspeakable sex practices of their people, is repeated in this century with a diversity of sex habits that would shame those ancient perverts, who were, in comparison to the moral lepers of the present, mere *dilettanti* in sex debasement.

Had a knowledge of sex and its purposes been taught those ancient people, society of today perhaps would not be honeycombed with so many loathsome diseases—nor accursed with the number of degenerates found everywhere. Sex seems always to have been a subject of apology and *perversion*, receiving consideration only when the *light was turned out*.

Can the wildest fanatic argue that we are better for this past long-continued neglect of so vital a subject? Is not the degradation and perversion of sex greatly increased by such a procedure? Is it not time to launch a movement to teach the creative laws, as first instituted by God, to groups and singly, in clubs, schools and churches, whether the majority agree or disagree? Light must be diffused on the darkness of this subject or the race will continue in ignorance and degradation.

If ignorance and secrecy were constructive and desirable, would not the people of the present be far in advance of the ancients, in morality and spirituality—spirituality being based on purity in sex—and race improvement? Most assuredly! Regrettably, the very reverse is true. Perversion is increasing to an alarming extent, though legal enactments and enforcements have to a degree scattered the red light districts and their denizens to the four winds of the earth, thereby greatly diffusing vice.

The "red light districts" to which the world points with scorn, and the subject of self-righteous suppression, are the least harmful in the perpetuation of perversion. The private life, in an uncountable number of homes the world over the entire face of the earth, reeks with defilement and corruption, not alone between men and women, but between men and men, women and women.

Society at large has little to fear from the inmates of the shadowed districts because, through police and medical supervision, they can be controlled and kept within certain limits. The woman of ill-fame does not, except in rare instances, reproduce her kind; consequently, her influence, compared to that of corrupt homes, is insignificant.

The greatest sex crimes in the human calendar are perpetuated *in the homes where love is not.* To enjoy, but not to bear children, and in defiance of the Lord's command: "Be fruitful," married couples resort to all manner of degrading practices. Perversion originates in the desire to prevent reproduction, without curtailing the pleasures of physical satisfaction. *This was the original sin, the first committed by Adam and Eve; it was the one "apple" they were forbidden to eat.*

Vice in the home is doubly destructive; bearing on the public good as well as on the future of the race. The ultimate result of unnatural practices on the individuals themselves are horrible to contemplate. Body, mind and Soul (if there is any) suffer; drugs being resorted to continually, the mind dwelling on debasing practices; the most diabolical of the effects being bequeathed to the children who frequently are born *despite the perversions.*

Has the student of methods for race betterment ever asked himself the question, with a mental attitude actually desiring the truth: "From where come all the cripples, idiots, drug fiends, degenerates and child and woman exploiters in the present society?"

We have already offered you the key to the supposed mystery; though it must *not* be inferred that we maintain the undefendable position that the perversion or sex sins of the parents are responsible for all cripples, idiots and drug fiends.

The enemies of the dissemination of sex knowledge declare that if instruction and publicity be directed toward this subject, the result will be far worse than the present position of humanity. Regrettable as this must appear to the humanitarian, the majority of mankind no doubt agree with this verdict.

It is a notorious fact that the majority are always against mental, physical and spiritual progression. Why? Because the greater number of human beings are satisfied to allow others to think and plan for them. They look backward to what their fathers thought and did, complacently accepting those conditions as good enough for themselves, rather than making the effort to help institute a higher order of living for their own and future generations.

It is the few who, imbued with the *Christic* spirit of helpfulness and service, step forward to lead their plodding and suffering brothers out of the land of bondage, prejudice, ignorance and bigotry, into a knowledge of God and His Laws. An understanding of the problems of sex is fully as essential and vital as is the knowledge of any other department of life.

When our youths are taught the facts concerning their bodies and their physical functions as clearly and carefully as students in agricultural colleges are instructed in the breeding and development of domestic animals; when sex-sanity and morality are considered as legitimate and as rational a study as Latin or Mathematics and far more important to the human race, *then vice will no longer be the destructive agency it is at present, because much of the mystery which first attracts the many, will have been dispelled.*

Mystery and curiosity travel hand in hand; secrecy is their

sponsor. The small boy who, untaught by his father, whispers
something obscene to his companion, laughing and gloating
over the vileness of the communication, is preparing for future
licentious desire and action. Being inquisitive, as all normal
children should be, *he seeks to know,* and wants to know and
discuss, that which seemingly, because his parents will not
enlighten him, is hidden.

In one way or another he will lift the veil; though generally
the knowledge he does obtain is not the truth, but an evil
interpretation of it. For this reason he succumbs to secret vice,
and another victim is added to the long list of the great god,
Ignorance.

Had his parents fulfilled their sacred trust, had the biological facts been taught him in a sane, orderly, reasonable,
decent manner, the evil side of the creative act might never
have entered his mind.

A very uncouth example illustrates the desirability of open-
ness, frankness, and correct understanding. When women wore
very long, clinging skirts, it was no uncommon sight to see
men and boys salaciously observing the shapeliness of limbs on
a windy day. All were animated by a natural curiosity, wanting to see that which is supposed to be concealed except in
the marriage chamber. Today, that particular phase of curiosity
is dead.

Women generally now wear skirts so short that pedal ex-
tremities have lost much of their allure. That which was once
so religiously concealed is now more than revealed; the
mystery is disclosed to all who may care to look.

The hideous, noxious, pernicious aspects of sex must be
erased from the minds of men, or the race will be foredoomed
through a purity turned to foulness. Whole nations *have* been

annihilated in the past, as both Biblical and profane history records, for this very reason. The story of the Israelites in the wilderness and the fall of the Roman Empire are ample proof that a people may be quickly wiped from the face of the earth, in repayment for sins of sex debasement.

God made the world and all it contains. He established laws for its welfare and then *pronounced all good.* In the wisdom of the Father certain edicts of sex were included; these He never revoked.

Some men would have us believe that He has now turned over an important department of life to be governed by the gross ignorance of men; that after having bestowed one of the greatest of His prerogatives on human kind, He has withdrawn Himself, thereby approving the chaos that has resulted.

The power to create, the privilege of generation and *re-generation* through right use of sex was not a whim or an accident of the great Creative God, but an eternal law given to men for a definite purpose, as fixed and unchangeable as that which governs the stars in their courses. Woe to that man, society, or nation, who or which attempts to subvert a law set into action by the Father of all.

The nations of the earth, now undermined with venereal diseases, can be enlightened and saved only through the education and direction of the individuals who compose them. Reverence and purity of desire are the first two requisites. Undoubtedly, these qualities were in the thought of the Nazarene when he said: "Unless ye become as little children ye can in no wise enter the Kingdom of heaven."

Men must return to, or re-acquire, the attitude of the child; the purity of mind and heart without which the laws and reason of sex cannot be correctly understood. It unquestionably requires a far stretch of the imagination to visualize the rehabilitation of the base, vulgar mind of a degenerate man, conceding the possibility of his return to the state of God-like purity possessed by the child-mind; *but unless he does,* he will remain a wreck and an outcast, and no power in earth or heaven, no faith or creed, can reach or save him.

Thousands upon thousands of these derelicts will continue in the path of destruction in spite of all that can be done to save them. The most that we can do is to look at them with an "unconscious" feeling of loathing, mingled with deep pity, and pass them by. Our responsibility is *to see to it that the younger generation is properly taught and rescued from this awful fate.* The children, still pure in thought, must be kept so.

Those whose thoughts and acts are now tainted with unholy desire must be turned toward the light of knowledge and the evil replaced with good. The young men and women must be appealed to; must be made to recognize the unhappy consequences of ignorance and, in the name of all that is Holy and Sacred, instructed in the exalted use of the reproductive functions of their being.

The older generations, fathers and mothers of the present, must be induced, through continuous inculcation of these truths, to recognize their responsibility, not alone in the preservation of their own minds and bodies, but likewise in the guidance of their offspring.

It must be thoroughly drilled into the minds of the young, middle aged and the old, that the entire sex function was organized by God and therefore cannot in itself be either unclean or impure. The use of the creative organism is just as normal as that of the stomach or any other part of the body. God did not create the function to be shunned or slighted; not to be the basis or the laboratory for obscene thoughts and actions; neither something to be ashamed of and degraded when darkness covers the earth, thus being catalogued as evil along with other destructive agencies that work in the night.

It is not an uplifting, ennobling thought for men, made in the image of the Father, to believe that He created them in such form, and with potencies for which they must forever be apologetic. Yet this is just what the majority of "he" and "she" creatures are continuously doing.

Sex in itself is pure. It is holy and exalting. When employed in the love-embrace its *potency is beyond compute.* In the right use of sex, in generation and REgeneration, man is endowed with a power angels might envy. Instead of striving to understand the laws governing this great privilege and possession of power, man continuously tramples this greatest gift of a just God in the mire of sensuality and degradation, thus failing even to realize the *holiness of the function,* the halo of glory that should attend its consummation; wallowing in perversion and voluntarily seeking the way to physical, moral and spiritual ruin.

Ignorance of the creative function is the sole cause for the general thought of impurity concerning it. Good and pure in itself, it has been besmirched by the "demons of sense gratification," until the thoughts of men are distorted and they see falsely as "through a glass darkly." Men, having defiled a benefaction of God, turn the use of a pure function into unholy channels and then declare sex manifestations unclean and unfit for those spiritually inclined.

It is utterly impossible for a healthy, normal, noble-minded man, who has employed his creative forces as the Creator intended he should, to think of sex with lewdness, or to consider it unholy or impure. To such an enlightened man (or woman), one part of the body is neither better, nor worse, than another. "Unto the pure *all* things are pure," said the Master-Teacher.

The development of a *superior race* must be brought about through the education of men in the correct and righteous use of the creative function; the fundamental laws must be freely taught, without bias, fear or favor.

God created all things in purity. The child's mind is pure, and will remain pure if sex and its *proper* exercise is explained to it before those who have debased the function, or who are totally ignorant of correct behavior, have had an opportunity to befoul the child's mind with lurid and highly inflammatory debasing stories.

Children have a right to truthful answers when they begin to ask questions regarding the creative organism. They should be told the truth about the powers and purposes of the sex nature. They must be so instructed on this subject that every detail is understood.

If the boy or girl receives a complete explanation from the parent, morbid and unhealthy thoughts will be defeated; mystery and speculation will be transmuted into knowledge; and the shameful, destructive practices and perversions will fade into nothingness as do dreams of the past.

THE BEGINNING OF SEX LIES

T IS legend that a noted prelate of one of America's most powerful organizations claimed that if his church could control the first nine years of a child's life, it mattered little what its later influences might be; the teachings of the church could never be eradicated from the child's mind or heart.

Generally this is true. The first impressions on the plastic mind of the child are indelible; but why confine the child's true education to the doctrines of any particular church or creed? Is it not more important to teach youths the *mysteries of being* than to drill into their minds the history of the saints; the necessity of observing special days in the church calendar or the preparation for an existence beyond the grave?[1]

Children are consistently taught the basic elements of a faith for the preservation of their Souls *after* death. The fundamentals of biology and sexology—having as their object the preservation of physical life, which is the basis, not only of health, happiness and evolution, but equally so of the *welfare of the Soul itself*—are almost entirely ignored and left to chance.

The Immortalization of the Soul is definitely related to the REgeneration of the body. It is just as imperative to know and obey God's laws governing the physical world as it is to follow the laws relating to the spiritual realms. How is it

---

[1] It is uncontradictable that if man lives *rightly* here on earth, then a fitting abode will be assured him after death, since the future is neither more nor less than a continuation of the present.

possible to build a resplendent future on a decayed present? Can an unclean mind and diseased body foster a pure and radiant Soul?

When a child is capable of questioning its parents concerning its origin, such inquiries are usually avoided or untruthfully answered. The perturbed, thoughtless, morally-ignorant mother or father attributes birth to "the stork," the doctor, the drug store or to some kind fairy, and hastily changes the subject.

Can a greater injury be inflicted on a confiding Soul than that of *deceiving a trustful child?* Is it not appalling to consider the foundationless falsehoods impressed upon the young child's mind by its ignorant parents at the very dawn of its intellectual awakening? When later the child becomes aware that it has been deceived, will it not doubt the truthfulness of the parents in all else?

The degradation of sex has its beginning at this very point. The child *will* soon be old enough to suspect something of the truth and is unlikely to forget the explanation made by its parents. Through companions equally ignorant, it will shortly be informed, in the most degrading manner, of the bald, vulgar aspects of the physical contacts of the sexes and the expectant results, and the heretofore unsullied mind becomes contaminated with filth and suspicion, never again to be restored to its pristine purity or faith in its parents and their veracity.

The child naturally concludes that the parents were ashamed of the creative act which called it into existence. It treasures to itself the great secret. Its imagination pictures the intimacy of human beings. The child, before its reasoning faculties have fully unfolded, is convinced that the method of creation must be an impure, unholy, and an unclean act; something to be ashamed of, veiled in falsehoods.

This condition, deplorable as it undoubtedly is, would not be so utterly hopeless, *if it ended here.* It does not. The corruption of thought and desire appeals to the lowest in the child nature, nurturing a hothouse growth of passionate inquisitiveness at an age when the urge of sex should be unknown, and the mind be yet thoroughly imbued with stories of fairies and fanes, gods and goddesses of fairy lands.

Secret vice quickly follows the broken faith in loved ones and the information obtained through vulgar companions. Ignorance of a law does not annul its effect. The indifference to duty and ignorance of the far-reaching effect of lies and evasion do not make parents any the less responsible.

Mothers and fathers are betrayers of their trust if they permit their children to be thrown upon the world untaught and therefore unprepared, to rightly use and control the powers of sex. An effect is always the result of a cause. If children grow into licentious men and women, or become debauchees and degenerates, finally ending in human wrecks, it surely indicates that there must be a sufficient cause to have produced such lamentable results.

What food for reflection this offers those who have the improvement of the race at heart and who grasp the significance of the possibilities to the race through the teaching of truth, in chaste language, to the children of men!

The intuition of a child is as active as that of its elders, if not more so. It therefore senses untruths quickly. The awakening of reason in the child induces many questions which are undoubtedly awkward to the youthful parents.[2] Every

---

[2] The parents may be ignorant, probably are, but it is their moral and religious duty—*an obligation*—to prepare themselves at least as fully as does the man who plans to engage in raising superior stock. With such preparation, they would then be prepared to answer, at least, all ordinary questions.

evasion only hinders the child's search for that knowledge which *inherently is its birthright,* and which it has a *right to demand,* and in confidence expect to receive without reservation.

Intuitively, the child senses when falsehoods, instead of truths, are given in answer to questions. The child is powerless to prevent its reasoning faculties from recognizing that it has been deliberately fooled; yet it cannot comprehend why a lie or evasion is offered when knowledge is sought. Instinctively the child questions those near its own age for answers to those unanswered questions which remain active in the mind. Who pays for the *"feeding of stones when bread was asked?"*

Many parents promise themselves that "when the child is older" they will have a "heart-to-heart" talk with it. Even if that resolution is kept and acted upon, it fails in its intended purpose. Before the child is old enough to talk "reasonably" with its parents, school companions, or older people, will already have commenced the demolition of the temple of purity, and the seeds of evil will be sown in the mind that might have been kept undefiled. It requires but few insinuations or vile suggestions to produce a turmoil in the imagination of a sensitive child.

Besides, there are now, as there always have been, men of the lowest type, who seduce and betray young boys and girls for their own sense-gratification. As an illustration, we cite one case which came under our observation. A boy who had been told the usual falsehood and forbidden to ask further questions, and whose seven years of life had failed to divulge the why and wherefore of his creation and existence, was thrown much into the companionship of a male creature past sixty years of age who had been introduced into the family as a permanent guest.

The house being small, the child shared a bed with the old man, who slowly, but surely, taught it all manner of vice whereby his own degenerate desires might be gratified. Ignorant of the right and the wrong, the boy was clay in the hands of a master potter. Warned to keep silent by the fiend, and fearing his parents, the child fell prey to debasing practices with the result that at twelve years of age he was a physical wreck and was brought to us for treatment. He told us the whole foul story. We found him fully developed, sexually, at twelve years. His entire nervous system was shattered; vision defective; a human wreck well on the road to a premature grave, at an age when he should have been reading the stories of cowboys or heroes.

The parents were speechless when confronted with the truth, though loathe to confess that they were the most guilty. "Pitiable!" you exclaim. Admittedly so, but *there are thousands upon thousands of just such cases developing continually, because of neglect and ignorance on the part of the parents.* Every form of vice "stalks abroad," seeking youthful victims. Parents not only leave every avenue open, but *invite the catastrophe.*

Referring to the case under discussion, it may be of interest to add that after a long period of readjustment, moral, mental and physical, this boy gradually regained his health and became a respectable member of society, but all faith in his parents was gone. Through a fault not his own, he had lost that feeling of tender and intimate companionship, kindness and love for men. Throughout life the inner self of that man will carry the ugly scars inflicted upon him in his youth as the result of the neglect of his parents.

The so-called innate goodness of a child cannot be depended

upon to protect it from the influence of vice. As a race, human beings are impregnated with perversions. From time immemorial the very atmosphere surrounding humanity has been saturated with thought-images of sex evils.

It is an exceptional case when the uninstructed, though innocent, child escapes the general contamination. Children are imaginative and imitative; possessing an inherent desire to expand their lives, gain experience and obtain information.

Witness how the ordinary child in school beams with pleasure over the acquirement of some special knowledge, or the details of some unusual event. It hastens home to pour into the ears of its mother every new discovery.

Especially is this true if that knowledge or event is in any way related to his own particular sensation or enjoyment. If to this supposed knowledge is added the idea of secrecy, the child-mind is enthralled. Is there any wonder, then, that it is enthralled by sex, as a mysterious, secret source of pleasure?

The carnal thoughts and destructive habits of past ages are inbred in the child nature of the present generation. The sex desires are hungers—a biological urge—of the physical being. As the physical nature in man is supreme, it logically follows that these *desires, appetites, and cravings* make themselves felt in the child mind with the first awakening of the sex consciousness.

Instead of the innate goodness in the boy and girl acting as a protective force, this inborn appetite of the creative energy impels it to seek ways and means for self-gratification without a thought of the result to itself or to others.

If the child reasons at all, it is in this manner: *"All those I know are practicing thus and so, seemingly enjoying it, and apparently deriving no ill effects; why should I not do likewise?"*

As a result, the child imitates the rest of its companions and pays the same penalty—a gradual degeneracy of body, mind, and that higher potency in man we term the Soul.

What is the remedy? Seek to learn the truth respecting all that concerns sex, and when your children commence to question you, follow your love instinct and tell them the *whole* truth, clothing it in words such as only mother-love can command.   Let it be similar to the following story-form:

"You can see this great world with its many men, women and children, its green trees, the beautiful flowers, birds and animals. There is another world in the distant beyond which the eyes of the body cannot see. In that great other world there are many Souls. To help you better understand what Souls are, we will call them children who have no father or mother, and who are more like good fairies. In their home they cannot think or do anything wicked, but only those things which little children should do if they love their mothers. In that home, instead of mothers, there are good women or angels who constantly watch over these little Souls. We call these good women their guardian angels. They come to earth with the children that come here.

"These little Souls seem to have everything they desire, but they cannot know either pleasure or pain.   They cannot know what it is to love a mother, or to be loved by one, because they possess no body such as we do, with which to feel, laugh or cry, and run to when in trouble.

"They see the children on earth romp and play among themselves or with animal pets, in their garden of flowers, with their little stubbed toes, mothers caressing and kissing their babies, seeing them retire to sleep, mothers listening to their prayers and fondly tucking them in their little beds.

"These little Souls of the other world then become dissatisfied with their heaven. They want to become like other little children, even though they may stub their toes, become sick, have pain and be made to cry; as well as having nice things to play with, and good things to eat, with mother loving and kissing them. This longing in the hearts of these little Souls gradually opens the way for them to come to this earth, so that they may have bodies like you and other children, but before they can come here, a place to receive them *must be carefully prepared.*

"Within your mother, God, who is the Father of the heaven to which all good fairies and Souls belong, and from which your father and mother came, has prepared a little temple which is to receive such little Souls as wish to come to earth. In this little temple within your mother, your father who loves her, and who desired a little child to love, sowed a tiny seed, which gradually began to grow.

"After a long time this seed within the temple of mother began to take the form of a little child. Then one day it was ready to leave the little temple and come forth, to be as other children.

"While this little body is growing, you, a fairy Soul in that other world, dissatisfied with your home there, were wishing to come to earth. Your guardian angel was always with, or near you, carefully watching so that nothing might happen to you. Then you were prepared for the long trip from fairyland to the earth-home, where father and mother, and the little body in the temple, was being prepared for you.

"Then one day, the glad tidings came that the body, the little house which you were to enter, would soon be ready. Your guardian angel prepared all the things which belonged to you and had you all ready for the trip when the call should come. At last came the day when you were told by the guardian angel to bid good-bye to all your companions and be ready to commence the journey.

"As you traveled from the land of Souls and Fairies, you quickly noted a change. In your former home it was warm and you could feel neither pain nor pleasure. You now approached a place where it was cold and you felt like crying. But you had little time to think, or to change your mind. You saw your mother who seemed to be very much larger than you expected. This almost frightened you, yet you were fascinated by your surroundings and your attention was held by the guardian angel who told you to be ready to meet your mother.

"Very soon the door of the temple was opened. It seemed to you that your mother suffered great pain. Then you saw coming from the temple which God had built in mother, a little body just like many you had so often seen in the arms of other mothers while you were yet in Fairyland.

"Your guardian angel told you to be ready as this was to be your home, and that with the first cry from the body you would 'fall asleep,' and that when you awoke you would feel heavy and cold, and would be hungry, and crying for the warm feeling which you had always known. Suddenly you became unconscious, and seemed to sleep for a long time.

"When you awoke everything seemed dark and cold. You heard yourself cry and did not know what to do because you could no longer move from place to place by simply wishing, as formerly. You called upon your guardian angel; but, though you could see her, she seemed to be at a distance and could not help you as she had been able to aid you before.

"Soon they washed and dressed you and you found your-self in mother's arms. Here you felt warm and found yourself gradually sinking into a peaceful sleep. You could still see your guardian angel, but as you came to know more of your mother, you could see less of your guardian angel. Now you no longer see her, though she is still watching over you as she did in that far-off Fairyland, and would feel deeply hurt if she saw you do things which displeased mother.

"This is the way all babies come to earth. Mother has told you this but it is not well for you to speak of it to other children as they might not understand. Let it be a sort of secret between you and your mother, and when other children wish to talk with you about these things, tell them only father and mother can understand them."

This is the truth as sacred philosophy teaches us, in language the child can grasp. To be sure, it may be clothed in other words, but it contains the answer to the oft-propounded question: "Mother, where did I come from?" If the one questioned has the true mother instinct, the mother love, she need not hesitate to tell the story to her child no matter what its age. If all mothers would answer their children honestly and without reservation, inviting their confidence and further questions, telling them not to listen to the stories voiced by other children, the basic foundation would be laid for a life that would know no shame.

Is this desirable and worth the effort? *It is!* Then let parents tell their children the truth and nothing but the truth; and one generation hence we will have abolished much of the ignorance and degeneracy so prevalent today.

We refuse to believe that the future will continue to produce the selfish, narrow-minded, ignorant, prudish parents of the present generation. There are men and women, ministers, teachers, writers, physicians, and lawyers, who have dedicated themselves to this movement of sex enlightenment and exaltation of the Creative function. These are thinking men and women who are ready to assume the place and responsibility of parents. They help to save many of the children of the present generation.

Because of the prejudice of the masses, and even many of the classes, the work will of necessity be hindered and many children prevented from receiving much-needed instruction; but the night of ignorance will be illuminated with understanding, thereby helping future generations. If all who but dimly perceive the light will *do their best,* the great work of race improvement, through the teaching of sex truths, will be spread. *The morning of a better day is dawning.*

SEX INSTRUCTIONS IN PUBLIC

From the Experience of Others, Learn Wisdom

ROM the experience of others, learn wisdom." This passage indicates that it is not necessary to suffer through our own experiences, if we are wise enough to profit from the acts and mistakes of our fellow men and the results produced from their efforts. Through this practice we are enabled to gain wisdom without being guilty of similar blunders.

In many departments of life we comprehend the law of cause and effect. In a great many others, in fact, in some of the most important activities in life, we totally ignore this law and gain knowledge only through bitter experiences.

Especially is this true with respect to practically everything that concerns the creative function. In the development of fancy cattle, prize poultry and pedigreed dogs, not to mention swine, we employ the most noted experts to teach us all the important details of mating, housing and feeding. We implicitly follow the instructions of such authorities to avoid loss, and because we believe their study and experiments qualify them as instructors.

In the infinitely more important department of human life— child culture and the development of a superior race—we not only fail to engage experts to discover for us the best food for the mother, the child, and the youth, but we refuse to listen to them when their services are offered gratis. We do *all* in our power to discourage them, bringing contempt upon all who dare to discuss the doctrine that the sex function is the port of entrance to the development of a superior race.

Often our demonstration does not end with contempt, but we mercilessly condemn, shun, and even persecute and imprison those who, through love for the unappreciative human race, dare to teach mankind the truth concerning themselves and their creative potentialities.

Why do we so avidly seek to learn all we can about animal husbandry; the proper mating, housing and feeding to insure production of the highest grade of chickens, hogs, dogs and cattle, while we condemn harshly those who would presume to teach us the science for the development of the human race?

Is it because we really consider the sub-human creatures of greater benefit to God and the Universe than his highest creation, which is man? Is it because the Creative powers and functions of the human race are less pure than those of the animals upon which we bestow such great care? These are issues we no longer *dare* evade.

In our public schools, even in some of the lower grades, we instruct the child in the mysteries of plant life—fertilization and culture—and believe this highly desirable for the child's future welfare. (Actually, the creative organism of the plant is in nowise greatly different from that of the animal creative and productive function.) We proceed along this line and in teaching horticulture, we instruct fully the dissection of the reproductive organism of the plant, explaining how fecundation, both natural and artificial, takes place.

Fundamentally, *there is little difference between the creative functioning of plant, animal and human. Why not then draw an analogy between the three departments of creation in chaste language, that child and adult can quickly comprehend the beauty, the chastity, the purity and the essentiality of sex?*

This would be the simplest, easiest and most desirable method of teaching the child, the parent and the public generally. The lecturer, when dealing with congregations of people, should instruct through the functional analogy of the plant which so closely resembles the human species. He can fully explain to his audience the reproductive organism of the plant, the method of fertilization, showing clearly the similarity between plant and animal, animal and human, and HOW WEAKNESSES AND DISEASES ARE AVOIDABLE while DESIRABLE TRAITS MAY BE BROUGHT INTO PROMINENCE.

In this manner the mind will conceive the wisdom of nature, unconscious of the morbid, destructive and carnal thoughts and desires usually aroused when sex is the subject of a lecture, or when problems associated with sex are publicly discussed.

Is this so difficult? Not in the least. Text books on the culture of plants may be obtained by anyone. Through a careful study of these text books anyone can readily become thoroughly acquainted with the problem. Add to this an acquaintance with animal husbandry, sex hygiene, eugenics and biology, and the individual is intelligently prepared to meet the problem.

Why has this not been the approved method of procedure? Why is this course not followed today? Because, for so many centuries man has been taught to ignore, and abhor, the sex question and all it represents. The most important side of the problem has never been even thought of, much less discussed. Universally, sex has been a subject of attention only when the sun had set and the light turned out so that "darkness covered the whole face of the earth."

The first necessity, therefore, is to arrive, through careful study, at a thorough understanding of the entire subject. Man must learn all that may be known of the exalted and spiritual side of sex. He must analyze with an open mind all that is learned; thus finding its desirable, constructive side, just as he seeks and finds the beauties in a highly developed flower.

In the consideration of this important question, we must avoid extremes; must ignore the dark side—that which brings dishonor, disease, misery, degradation and death—though willing to give it the recognition which its possibilities for evil demands.

We should likewise religiously avoid discussions in season and out of season, bearing in mind the Biblical injunction: "There is a time and a season for all things." We should discourage the discussion of the sex question in public gatherings of mixed audiences unless it happens to be a meeting called for that express purpose.

At the moment when humanity is awakening to the tremendous importance of sex hygiene, there are many opportunities to inculcate the truth, but we should be extremely careful to do this in a dignified manner as becomes true and enlightened men and women. We should never make reference to anything concerning sex in a ribald, or what might appear, vulgar manner; nor by giving our silent consent to others who may be guilty, thereby doing grave injury to the cause for the development of a superior race.

In attempting to discuss this great and vital subject before the people, whether a gathering of those who desire to become teachers, parents, or children having reached the age of comprehension of so important a subject, we must honor it by our personal appearance. The discussion must be dignified, fearless and honest, to impress upon the minds of the audience the necessity for the truths embracing the Divine Creation and the glory of race regeneration.

If those to whom we bring this important information are not fully informed, we should begin our instructions by means of analogy; thence proceed to the sub-human, and gradually unfold the mystery of the creative ability and organism of the human. We must illustrate in simple language the purpose and power of each organ of creation, designating them by comprehensive names readily understood by the audience, yet far removed from the vulgar expressions familiar to every boy and girl in school.

The greatest success, especially before young people, depends upon our appearance as a speaker, and the manner in which the subject is presented. If we are thoroughly conversant with the entire problem, if we are at ease, free from self-consciousness, and, *if we believe all that we teach,* then it will not be difficult to inculcate in the young the belief that sex, in all its offices, is both sacred and divine.

The most difficult phase of our work will be to prove to man, woman and youth, that sex is NOT the degraded *avenue of passion* it has always been taught, or believed to be; an inheritance heartily to be ashamed of—but man's *highest and holiest gift from a Creative God.*

Sex, admittedly, has a dark, a *very* dark side. The perversion of sex has brought disease and degradation to countless numbers. The exaltation of the same potential force will bring health, longevity, and Immortalization. Like all forces in nature, it is dual in its potentialities and manifestations, depending entirely upon the method of exercise. It is left to the *free choice* of individuals, whether they will employ this power for a glorious realization, or degrading death, with the possibility of utter destruction of the Soul itself.

How many would think of using a prayer to curse another? Though there are many men who have lost all respect for religion and disclaim belief in God, yet few of these could be induced to voice a prayer for the purpose of calling down a curse upon another. Why? Because through their entire life they have been taught that prayer is for but one purpose; either to ask God for a favor, or for requesting a blessing upon another.

There is but one universally-accepted meaning attached to prayer; and that is for good. As a matter of fact, prayer or supplication may be as readily voiced in calling forth a curse upon another as in invoking a blessing; but, fortunately, the race has been taught only its higher purpose.

As with prayer, so with the procreative function. If once we can bring mankind to a realization that sex is a blessing and not a curse; a thing of beauty and not an abomination; if we can instill a full comprehension that sex is like a prayer, pure in itself, holy in all its natural functions, and for good only, then will mankind conceive sex in an entirely different light. Up to the present the accursed idea of sex has been the only side presented to humanity, while the good has been ignored, and even denied as having existence.

Within recent years men have gone rampant on business efficiency, taking the position that what is usually termed "personal magnetism" is the basis of force and power underlying the mental brilliancy and alertness necessary to attain success in any line of endeavor. Only a few of these "preachers of a constructive gospel" are actually aware that this so-called "personal magnetism" is neither more nor less than an underlying sex capacity; that the more fully this is developed, controlled and wisely directed, the greater the power, force and energy, alertness and brilliancy of mind, possessed.

In reality, the basis of achievement in every line of endeavor, is *virile* force; virility being the result of creative ability. As the sex powers diminish, so will the creative power and "personal magnetism" diminish. In the sense as here used, the phrase "creative power" has reference to the capacity to accomplish, to succeed, where others fail.

Like with man, so with woman. In her this force manifests itself by the fire in her eyes; the freshness of her skin; the glory of her hair; the vivacity of her nature; the enchantment of her smile. We speak of her as "full of life," but few understand that all these attractive qualities are actually and fundamentally based upon a healthy sex nature, on an organism functioning normally.

Who is able to behold anything abnormal in such a man or such a woman? On the contrary, do we not speak of them as perfect, as examples all would do well to emulate? Not for one moment do we associate their personality with the healthfulness and naturalness of the creative functions; though as an uncontradictable fact, all that is desirable in their entire being is based absolutely on the creative potency, naturally, normally, healthy and fully developed.

Having the knowledge of these principles, it is our sacred duty to teach the truth to every member of every audience before whom it is our privilege to appear. We must prove to our listeners, to the full extent of our ability, that these desirable qualities in man depend upon a normal, healthy and fully developed sex nature.

Sex must not be abused, else the penalty is fearful to contemplate. If we can induce men and women, fathers and mothers, boys and girls, to comprehend this great truth, and show them that exalted sex is the foundation of a true life, and the true power of attraction, then we will have removed from their mind that dark and sinister side which has held man in bondage for so many centuries.

Those who have abused the creative privileges granted them by the Creator, look upon the function with shame. These are the individuals who are always loudest in their denunciation of all instructions concerning sex. "To the pure in heart all things are pure," but they have misused their sacred privileges and the "veil of purity" has fallen from their eyes. Like Paul before his conversion, they "see with eyes darkly."

The individual who employs his creative functions for ignoble purposes poisons the Fountain of Life and creates a diseased mind, a perverted imagination, and a darkening aspect of the subject. That misuse brings shame is clearly illustrated in the Biblical allegory of the Garden of Eden episode. While Eve loved the natural life, she saw nothing impure, or to be ashamed of, in her nudity.

To both her and to her partner Adam, their bodies were pure, holy, created by God in the highest art; but the moment they abused their creative nature, by indulgence for the satisfaction of passion, without a desire for generation or regeneration; and with the effort to *prevent the natural consequence of the act[1],* their minds became assailed with a sense of shame and their nudity became as a "nakedness which had to be concealed."

In this one story illustrating the result following the abuse

---

[1] Those honestly and sincerely seeking the truth should obtain a good Bible Concordance and check up on all references in the Bible to the "seed." They will be surprised and astonished; also greatly enlightened.

of the creative power, we can find material for a thousand sermons. It proves conclusively that it is not the pure in heart and clean in mind who condemn true sex science, but those who, through immoral relations, have discovered their own nakedness.

In the light of their own "nakedness" they see all others; polluted and defiled in the sight of God their Creator who, in calling them forth, saw that "all was good." How will these answer their God when He demands of them: "What hast thou done with the talents (creative ability) I gave thee?"

Sex is like a good medicine which, when rightly employed, induces health; but wrongly used produces disease, misery and death. The creative function is, in itself, pure and holy. When sex is correctly utilized it is a means of generation as well as for REgeneration—a rebuilding of the entire being. When sex is abused, it is like poison to the mental faculties; it colors the imagination darkly; induces morbidity; beclouds the imaginative faculty of the mind; brings sorrow and misery; ending in death, if not in total extinction. It is not the power that is to be condemned, but the vile and carnal mis-use men make of it.

The potency of this force for either good or evil is readily illustrated. A young man living a natural life is full of vitality and vital force; call it "personal magnetism" if you will. He readily attracts people. He easily retains his friends and accomplishes that which seems impossible to others. He quickly passes hundreds on the way who are apparently much more talented. He does his work simply, naturally and unconsciously. It seems as though the gods and fates are continually smiling upon him.

Through some unwise association this same young man contracts habits destructive to his well-being. He misuses the creative functions; he drains his vitality through pleasure-able exercises. Gradually the fire fades from his eyes, his attractiveness leaves him, his friends feel he has changed and he is no longer magnetic. The work formerly accomplished with ease becomes labor; his appearance of youth gives place to that of old age. Why this great change? Because he has degraded his "inheritance," depleted the "storage batteries" of life and has reaped the results of his disobedience.

This is one of the most emphatic lessons indicating the desirability of a powerful development of the sex nature, and how important it is that this most valuable possession be correctly used for creative *and* re-creative purposes only; *never* for the satisfaction of desire alone. Passion alone is ignoble, resulting in weakness and disease, finally ending in death.

Here is the all-important question. WHO *is* to teach sex to young and old? The first thought suggests "the public schools and institutions of higher learning," but we are fully aware that all too many of them are honeycombed by the Communists and fellow travelers who do not believe in God, but discourage such belief by every device within their power.

These therefore do not hold anything sacred. To them sex certainly is not in any sense spiritual. They most certainly are *not* the proper mediums for this purpose. True, they are capable of teaching biology, this being based on Natural Science, but further than that they cannot go.

Where then are we to seek for those fitted for this great and important work?

The field narrows down to the men of God, those who truly believe the "Word of God" in all its aspects and recognize the Divine Law as sacred. Unfortunately, all too many of these shun the Sacred teachings of the Bible as they would a rattle-snake. They have not dared to delve into the sex teachings of the Bible. Few know the difference between the "holy" and "unholy" use of the "seed" implanted in man by God. Until they study the sex teachings of the Bible, they lack all under-standing of the "Great Sin." They know little or nothing of REgeneration, or of changing man's "mortality into Immor-tality."

The Sacredness of sex, hence the right use of sex, the Holi-ness of sex and the Spirituality of sex, can be taught only with safety by men ordained *by* God who are willing to face facts, tell the truth and teach the truth to mankind without hesitation.

Let the public schools and institutions of higher learning teach biology and the mechanics of sex, while the Priests of God teach the spiritual, REgenerative science of SEX. Only in this manner can mankind in general become fully acquainted with the true *mysteries of life.*

DANGEROUS PERIOD OF LIFE
PUBERTY

UBERTY is that period in the life of a girl when her procreative organism has reached the development necessary to function as required by Nature for the conception of a new being. Undoubtedly, Nature had primarily intended that when this stage was reached she should have attained full bodily growth, and be prepared to do her full duty as a member of the human family.

It is likewise the period of her life—*and this is most important*—when her parents are no longer responsible before God for her action, and she herself must assume full responsibility for her thoughts, desires and acts.

Unfortunately, in all too many instances, the laws governing the development of the body have not kept pace with those giving life and activity to the creative functions, and at this age it is possible for almost any girl to conceive, three or five years before her physical structure is fully developed.

Because of this anomaly the physical body is that of a girl who should be happy with her dolls or in the companionship of other boys and girls, while the mind and desires are those of a fully developed woman.

When a girl has reached this stage of life we find it difficult to keep her innocent in thought and free from acts which might be wholly to her detriment in later life. On this account, the period during puberty is most dangerous. Every care must be exercised by the mother or guardian to avoid any misstep that might lead the girl astray and ruin her chances for happiness.

A few months before the beginning of puberty we have a girl wholly carefree and happy, and undisturbed by any feeling of self-consciousness in the companionship of boys. She takes part in their games and sports with carefree abandon, possibly failing to recognize, at least consciously, that there is a difference between the sexes. Then, almost imperceptibly a change takes place. A transformation of her entire being is in process. Her mental attitude changes, with surprising suddenness, from that of a boyish girl, into that of a woman, and here is the danger: she is torn between the feelings of the boyish girl and that of the awakening woman.

With the awakening of sex activity (biological urge and longing for affection), life appears totally different from what it seemed but a short time before; bewilderment and painful self-consciousness takes the place of the former instinctive activity.

The girl may be likened to the uncouth youth, who is aware that there is a correct way to enter a room filled with people, but unable to properly proceed; the greater his effort to appear self-possessed and self-confident, the more likely he is to act awkwardly and ungainly. The girl is fully conscious that the former indiscriminate carefree association with those of the opposite sex can no longer be continued, but she is uninformed as to just what is the proper thing to do and how to go about it.

Long before this period in the girl's life the wise mother will have informed her daughter of just what to expect; when and in what manner to expect it and what should be done to meet the situation. Happy and fortunate is the mother who has not failed her daughter and allowed her to obtain such information from associates or older persons ignorant of the true facts, for to such misleading information can be traced much of the sorrow and misery responsible for the suffering of so many women.

The paralyzing effect this unexpected phenomenon has on her mind makes her incapable of clear thinking. In her ignorance, she assumes that her experience is unique and that even if she were to confide in her parents, and tell them of the condition, they probably would misunderstand and misjudge. Thrown on her own resources, she reasons from past experience; she remembers that whenever there was a flow of blood for any reason the first thing to look for was a cloth and *cold* water. She secures the cold water, applies it until the flow ceases, and by this very act often lays the foundation for future illness.

Had she been instructed in the anatomy, physiology and natural functions of the creative organism and told that at a certain period of her life the ovaries prepare the ovum or human egg; that preceding the passing of this ovum from the ovary discharging to the uterus *via* the Fallopian tubes, where it may be impregnated and become a human, there is a flow of mucous and blood preparing the passage; that this blood will be discharged from the vagina—had she been fully informed to expect this at some time or another and how to proceed when the condition made its appearance, she would have been prepared for this "dark," though altogether natural, period of her life.

Moreover, almost any mother can anticipate this event by certain almost unmistakable "signs" that manifest in the behavior of her daughter; actions all clearly indicative of what is to be expected. The symptoms most often manifesting are the various mental peculiarities, since the physiological foundation of menstruation rests in the nervous system. This affects the entire nervous system and reflects on the mental reactions by erratic activity. The appetite frequently becomes irregular, or, as is often the case, there may be a craving for certain foods clearly not conducive to health and well-being. Often there is great langour, backache, pain in various parts of the body, chills, headache, morbidity, perversity of action and irritability.

When such symptoms are evident in the girl of ten to fourteen years of age the mother should be prepared with her sanitary cloths and napkins, and kindly inform the daughter that at the first symptom of the unusual, she is to come to her that she may be fully prepared for what is the greatest event in her life: the change from girlhood into womanhood; from innocence into responsibility.

Finally, when the expected symptoms appear, the girl should be induced to retire to her room and recline on a bed or couch. Common remedies, according to the symptoms manifesting, should be prescribed. If there are chills and slight feverishness, hot teas should be given until these symptoms disappear and the flow becomes normal, after which the girl should be allowed to remain quiet for several days.

If the inception of the menstrual flow of the girl is anticipated, properly prepared for, and correctly taken care of, the cause of future trouble will have been eliminated. The menses, once naturally established, become a normal function of the female organism and seldom cause trouble.

How vastly different from the usual chain of events! We have in mind a case that will clearly illustrate this. A family of four, two boys and two girls; the mother an average American, who had been taught nothing when a girl and whose only knowledge was her own experience, taking it for granted that just as she had to learn the "hard way," so must her daughters.

The older of the two girls, at the age of thirteen and while romping and playing with her brothers and several neighborhood boys, suddenly became aware that conditions were not as usual with her. There appeared nothing unusual so far as her physical well-being was concerned but, as she expressed it, "something warm seemed to flow."

Almost unconsciously she placed her hand to the mouth of the vagina, and, on withdrawing, found it covered with blood. Naturally, she was dumbfounded and did not know what move to make. In this dilemma she turned to her companions who were as ignorant, and happily, as innocent as she. The concurrent conclusion arrived by the consultation was that the best thing to do was to secure a cloth and cold water; that possibly it was no more than an ordinary nosebleed with which they were familiar.

The cloth and cold water were secured and applied, with the result that the flow ceased and a chill set in, the child having been perspiring freely, due to exercise. When the time came for the next periodical flow, there was no indication of it, but instead a chill and swelling of the limbs. A physician was consulted. He suspected something out of the ordinary; questioned the girl until she informed him of the former occurrence. For many years thereafter this girl suffered severely at each monthly period, all due to the failure of the mother to properly instruct her. If the mother herself were ignorant then she should have taken the girl to the family physician for proper instructions.

Occurrences of this nature are well nigh universal, which certainly does not speak well for our twentieth century enlightenment and our boast of being intelligently informed on all important subjects. It is distinctly *not* an honor to us to be forced to admit that more than nine-tenths of our girls reach the age of puberty without the slightest knowledge of the phenomena of life before them.

Nor is it an honor to motherhood, that girls, because of their ignorance, should attempt to hide, for fear of unjust accusations, what every girl should look forward to with as great a pride as the young man does to his first long trousers—an emblem of womanhood on her part; on his, a symbol of manhood.

Not all motherhood is based on ignorance. We have in mind a mother of the enlightened age; one blessed with several daughters who do her honor. She is not merely the human machine who prepares their food and looks after their clothing—she is also their companion. Just as these girls come to their mother with their studies, so do they go to her with their confessions, their problems and their questionings.

If Johnny Jones happens to display his wisdom of the world and gives expression to some remark they do not understand, they appeal to their mother for an interpretation. She, wise mother, instead of showing self-consciousness on her part and telling them to be ashamed to repeat "such a remark," tells them just what he did mean and then proceeds to give them a full explanation of it in language chaste and pure.

These girls never ask a companion for an explanation of a remark they do not understand. They wait until evening and then appeal to the mother, who, as will be universal in the good time coming, is also their confessor.

These girls have been instructed in biology, anatomy and physiology. They comprehend the mysteries of creation and have been told of the coming event when they will bid goodbye to childhood and enter girlhood.

One of the girls, complaining of flushes and a feeling of dizziness, was promptly kept home from school so she might rest. Upon informing the mother of the appearance of a discharge, she was shown how to apply the sanitary cloth; how to change it; and taught the correct method of bathing locally with warm water and sponging the entire body with tepid water once each day.

The next day, instead of being sent to school, she was allowed to stay at home and rest, thus freeing the mental and nervous system from the strain always resultant from forced study during this trying time.

This wise and knowing mother never allows her daughters to attend school during these periods, but tells them to rest, play games, have music and to generally enjoy themselves.

What is the result? The development of these girls is at its best; there is no nervous irritability; no irrational action; no morbidity; they are happy and carefree, and seldom are aware of the periodic flow, aside from the necessity of changing sanitary napkins, and keeping the body free from undesirable odors. Here, briefly, are the fruits of proper guidance by a normal, enlightened, twentieth century mother.

Our present day educational system is fundamentally wrong and destructive in its tendency. It is diametrically contrary to the laws governing normal boyhood and girlhood; laws that should be well understood by every physician and educator:

First: Boys during adolescence are extremely active and, to develop normally, must be continually occupied with exercises, recreations and studies, so that by the hour for retiring they are sufficiently tired to be ready for sleep. This routine will be a preventive for undesirable habits, or at least will modify them, and reduce the possibility of their becoming a menace to boyhood and the cause of weakness in later life.

Second: Since the physiologic base of menstruation stems from the nervous system, it is necessary, if the welfare of the girl is to be considered, that a directly opposite method of procedure be followed in her consideration. Instead of urging her to activity and intensive study, as we should do with boys, it is essential to as nearly as possible allow her complete rest during the four or five-day menstruation period, nor dare we incite her to difficult mental activity either directly before or after the monthly period.

Our present system is to consider boys and girls during adolescence and puberty as exactly alike in their natures, desires, tendencies, mental capacities and physical endurance when, as previously stated, they are directly the opposite. The treatment accorded them must be diametrically different if good is to result.

This cannot be successfully contradicted. In the name of reason and common sense, how can we expect a healthy womanhood and normal motherhood if we accord the girls in school the treatment we should prescribe only for the boys; a treatment which all too often completely shatters the nervous system, weakens the mentality, and breaks down the moral stamina?

At the time of the transition from girlhood to womanhood other radical changes take place. Instead of continuing her companionship with the boys as formerly, hugging and kissing them, and taking part in all their games, the normal girl withdraws within herself, she becomes shy and self-conscious, no longer the jolly good fellow and happy playmate.

The boys, unable to understand this change in her attitude, are inclined to ridicule her, making her the target for their jests and jibes; irritating her and creating in her an abnormal sensitiveness, possibly leading to permanent injury; all of this might be avoided were the girl properly instructed and told what to expect and how to meet the situation.

At this juncture her imagination also begins to unfold, as the creative nature asserts itself. She becomes conscious of strange desires within herself. Having, as yet, no real comprehension of love, she does possess, intuitively, a knowledge that there exists an indefinable something which would give her pleasure and a feeling of satisfaction; *the womanly longing to be possessed.* This feeling is intensified when in the presence of a male companion whom she respects. Whether she realizes it, or not, she is now approaching the brink of a dangerous period in her life, and unless she is fully prepared, she is liable to commit serious errors that may affect her entire life.

As an instance, if in company with a youth or man she likes, and who may not be thoroughly honorable, she may easily be aroused to desires which are as yet a mystery to her. These desires may become so strong as to cause her to comply with her companion's wishes and she, as a result of the indiscretion, enters the rank of unwilling, unconscious, and unhappy motherhood, though wholly innocent in thought or intent. Should this happen, society will discard and condemn her, when in truth, she is as innocent before God as the day she was born. Those whose duty it was to instruct, prepare and guard her, alone are guilty.

Besides instructing our girls in sexology, we must at the same time, enlighten them on the many and varied changes that will take place in their innermost beings and how to bravely meet and overcome any questionable tendencies by constant occupation, exercise, games, social intercourse, recreation, music, plays free from morbid or immoral suggestions, etc. If we will instruct them in all these details, as well as on how to avoid having the passions aroused beyond control, our duty will have been well performed and we need have little fear for their safety.

Here are some practical recommendations. In all too many instances, tuberculosis, anemia or *Green* sickness, and other serious ailments develop in the girl approaching, or entering, adolescence. Immediately on the appearance of any symptoms of weakness or illness, a reliable physician should be consulted. In many instances endocrine treatment is indicated. If this is recognized and the proper measures taken, much can be done to prevent a lifetime of weakness, illness and misery.

MARRIAGE

THE WEDDING NIGHT

"He who begins with his wife with rape is lost."—Arabian.

ITHOUT DOUBT, the great majority of men have been doing this very thing on their wedding night, and, as a result of this tragic beginning, were never again able to rewin the respect and affection their wives had for them as sweethearts.

Women, with certain exceptions, are peculiarly constituted by their Creator. It matters little how greatly a woman may love, how deep her longing to be *possessed*, or how ready and even anxious she may be to give herself to the embrace; she nevertheless expects her suitor to entreat her for the favor requested; *secretly hoping that he will not give up until he has caressed her into submission.*

This instinct, longing or desire, call it what we will, is *born in the heart of every real, desirable, womanly woman.* All men can well make this great, vital truth a part of their lover's creed. If a man is truly a *man*, as he expects the woman to be a *woman*, and if he but partially understands her—what man can do more—he will play his part of the lover with knightly bearing and with forebearance.

He will feel within himself that she has a right to expect this small consideration from him if his desire merits her compliance and in doing his part, it is certain that an understanding of the innermost desire of her nature will return many pleasures and blessings.

The sorrows and unhappiness rampant in the lives of the vast majority of married couples can be traced to the *way* of approach on the wedding night. Whether the wrong approach is due to ignorance or lack of manhood does not matter.

Generally speaking, the average man has in mind but one predominant idea: compliance with the privilege he believes to be his. He never gives a thought as to *why* this privilege should belong to him.

He is totally unaware of the duties devolving upon him with the compliance of the favors he seeks or expects. He foolishly imagines—if he thinks about it at all—that his whole duty has been fulfilled in the fact that the woman of his choice has consented to become his wife; that he has married her and is providing a home for her together with the necessities of life.

In exchange for all this he feels that she is forthwith and thereafter bound to take care of his home, grant his requests when he is so minded, and both bear and care for his children when they accidentally result from his embraces.

All too often the woman is equally at fault; expecting a home, the possessions which make life desirable, with very little self-denial on her part, but much love and affection, in return or exchange for the least possible effort on her part.

Laboring under such false conceptions relative to their respective duties and privileges, the average man and woman are wed; enter the marriage chamber; and emerge in the morning, very much the wiser, though a great deal sadder for their experience of a few short hours, a feeling of mutual disgust ensues, with a cooling love for him on her side, and dissatisfaction with her on his side.

As an illustration, let us cite a case of which we happen to possess all the facts:

The young man we have in mind looked upon woman as the queen of heaven; would not believe that any woman could stoop to sell her body, and had an idea that all women were very much misunderstood—in which last supposition, of course, he was more or less correct. This youngster had some knowledge of sex laws, though totally ignorant of the wisdom which makes man a successful lover. He "fell in love" with a young lady of nearly his own age and believing his emotion fully reciprocated, married her.

They entered the bridal chamber, and like all of his kind— naturally so—he requested, caressed and coaxed for the privilege of a complete consummation of the marriage rite. Do what he would, the lady refused, turning away from him. She rather coldly informed him that had she married a young man of her acquaintance (a former suitor), she felt that he would have loved her without making such a request.

The husband's ideals relative to women, love, marriage and the inception and birth of children were extremely high. He never would have given a thought to marriage had he entertained the slightest doubt that he had the love of the woman.

It is easy therefore to picture the effect such a statement had upon him. It chilled him to the very center of his Soul, and the love he formerly had for the woman who was now his wife suffered a shock from which he never fully recovered. The memory of the incident remained to haunt him and to loom up ghost-like when thereafter he was prompted to repeat his request.

This experience is merely an example of countless others, with slight variation one way or another, that occur daily throughout the world. In the main, such cases come as a direct result of the faulty instructions girls receive from their mothers. Many of these mothers are themselves frigid by nature, having been begotten by mothers cold and embittered in heart, who were ignorant enough to instruct their daughters in the delusion that between man and woman love can exist independent of sex or its consummation. This is the most dangerous delusion under which a girl can labor. It is wholly devoid of truth and will most certainly prove destructive to her happiness if she attempts to govern her actions accordingly.

The girl should be minutely instructed in both her duties and her rights before she enters the bonds of wedlock. She must be clearly informed that passion is not love; that it can exist without love, and that when satisfied there is no longer any desire for the companionship of the one who served as the victim in its appeasement.

But, what is of greater importance to a girl and happiness, is the realization that while there is love without passion among the angels, and a semblance of the divine emotion in the weak and impotent, yet without passion there can be no such ecstacy in the hearts of *real* men and women.

Nature has seen fit to base conjugal love in companionship with passion; that there might be desire for possession on his part, and a longing to be possessed on her part, thereby assuring the propagation of the species.

She must also be taught that when man loves, coaxes and caresses her, the duty and love she bears him make it incumbent upon her to grant his *reasonable* requests.

Every woman, before her marriage, must be fully instructed in the consequences of the rite. Basically, it is an expression of love, having for its consummation generation or REgeneration. Under these conditions gratification and enjoyment are necessary for her well being. She must be impressed with the all-important fact that the embrace should never be undertaken merely for the satisfaction of passion alone.

Love must primarily be the incentive, then some great desire, such as health, happiness or long life, must be firmly concentrated in the mind. Likewise must she be informed of the possibility of pain to be endured during the first, or first few marital embraces. It is the birth of a new condition; the opening of a new world to her; both natural and normal in every respect.

It is also necessary to impress on her mind the desirability of conserving her modesty, that she should never neglect her appearance but continue all that has charmed her husband; observing propriety in the matter of dress and undress, forever enshrouding herself in a veil of mystery so that she will not become commonplace in his sight. Apparently these are insignificant details, but upon them often hangs the hope of conjugal happiness.

Instructions to the man are of equal importance if happiness is to result from the union. He must be made conscious of the absolute uncontradictable fact that although he has considered himself lord of creation, there are a multitude of privileges belonging to him which he has *no* right to *demand,* though he may possess them if he can win them. It must be firmly impressed upon his mind that if he expects to retain a woman's love he must at all times respect her modesty. He should never attempt to uncover her unless she clearly indicates her desire; nor may he insist on the enjoyment of the sexual exercise, *especially on the wedding night,* but must win compliance by coaxing, caresses and loving attention; that failing, to deny himself such gratification—to be later repaid many times for his self-control and patience.

He must be taught that a woman, even if she be his wife, may many times for good reasons of her own, refuse his requests even when she herself desires the embrace, and by continuing his caresses without further requests, he can often win her consent. He must use discretion in grasping a situation when she has cause for non-compliance, and cease his attention altogether for that time.

Rarely does a young man realize, until too late, after love has been destroyed, that in the beginning of marriage there may be far more unpleasantness than pleasure for the woman and that she complies with his requests merely because of her love for him. It is at this time he must show the greatest gentleness; brute force may induce in her a sense of loathing for him, while understanding and sympathy will win her respect and bring him greater love.

An important lesson which *most* young men fail to learn is the fact that all normal women want and appreciate admiration of their person. There is not a full-blooded woman living who does not feel that the man who professes to love her should likewise cherish her form and think it admirable. If he fails to do this he will eventually regret his lack of appreciation.

A man should quickly appreciate the fact that though the woman of his bosom comprehends little or nothing relative to the rights and privileges belonging to her, *she instinctively understands the art of love.* This feeling or longing for love is inborn, and with her it is *the open door to all she possesses.*

If she is offered love, she will reciprocate by giving her all; by granting every desired privilege even to the extent of willingly sacrificing herself as well as her honor. Woman, by her very nature, is love personified, although this personification is frequently degraded. While man thinks of himself, of achievements, of his business and the thousand and one other details of life, she thinks only of her love. This is why his little attentions, his admiration and caresses are so welcome and so highly treasured.

Man's life is his business. Through force of circumstances the most affectionate man living often appears to accept love as merely a side issue. This is *seldom because his love is less sincere and less true than a woman's,* but because he is the protector of his home and the one upon whom devolves the necessity of supplying the needs of the family.

In this he resembles the primitive man who often was obliged to leave wife and family for weeks at a time to secure the food they required. He did not voluntarily deny himself their companionship; necessity compelled him to do so.

Similarly the man of affairs must meet the keen competition of today and center his entire mind and whole attention on the achievement of success. Apparently he does not think of his wife, but deep in his consciousness there is an abiding love which manifests through his efforts to *accomplish for her sake.*

Should he at times forget the REgenerative Law of his being and request favors without the usual caresses, she must not hastily conclude that his love has waned or be foolish enough to accuse him of having in mind merely the gratification of his senses. *This has led to countless disasters.*

Woman's intuition is usually correct if her personal feelings do not becloud it, and will tell whether he really has ceased to care, or his action merely an oversight of which *all* men are sometimes guilty. Although it may be necessary or advisable for her to call his attention to his seeming carelessness, she should be tactful in her manner and not accuse him of a deliberate neglect of which he is really innocent.

Another source of much sorrow, and possibly the greatest test of his love for her, comes through opinions voiced, accusations made and slights offered by her when in erratic moods. *If a man is wise he will ignore these periods and every act and spoken word connected with them,* thereby preserving his own happiness and peace of mind, and ultimately earning her gratitude for his consideration.

A common complaint of men to their friends and physicians is that their wives generally choose the time during the marriage rite to tell them of their faults and weaknesses, or accuse them of unfaithfulness. This practice is *most* destructive to marital happiness and if continued is certain to create inharmony and mental unbalance.

The *one time* in a man's life when he *really* desires peace and contentment is while engaged in the love embrace. It is during this period that the mind should be wholly free from all external and disturbing thoughts and be centered on some great desire in *addition* to that for love satisfaction.

The woman who is foolish or ignorant enough to scold, find fault, or accuse during this *sacred* moment is certain to gradually lose the love of her husband. This is *equally* true when circumstances are reversed.

We offer no sympathy for the man who is vain enough to think he has the right to demand obedience from his wife relative to the marital embrace, and who fails to approach her with love and caresses. Such a man does not manifest manhood, or deserve the love of any good woman.

Without passion there can be no true and lasting love between the sexes, passion being the basis, the *fire* of love. Granting this, we emphatically state that there is no excuse for over-indulgence of the passionate nature. Love itself may be manifested at times by other means than the embrace; and because a man caresses his wife daily is no reason he should that frequently be permitted indulgence in the marriage rite. The good Book informs us: *There is a time and a season for all things.* While there may be endearments and caresses whenever opportunity offers, exercise of the rite itself should not be sufficiently frequent to induce weakness. It should never be undertaken while there is either ill-feeling or a misunderstanding between the two, as this poisons mind and body and gradually builds up resentment one toward the other.

One of the most important requisites for the newly-married pair to learn is the necessity of controlling the passion if the union is to be a happy one. This applies to the woman no less than to man.

The theory that woman is usually passionless is wholly wrong, or if true, is regrettable. Youthful married people who have not been properly instructed in this respect are apt to fall into error and the embrace becomes an enervating habit rather than constructive exercise of the creative function. They must quickly realize that marriage does not give them the privilege of indulging to satiation; no individual should be guilty of such abuse and the marriage ceremony does not grant any right to do so.

It is the law in the creative realm that the more frequently the desire of the male in youth is gratified the oftener will there be a desire for indulgence. There should be a covenant between the twain, stipulating that the Rite may be indulged only so many times a week. If this is respected, their self-denial will be amply rewarded.

We do not mean to imply that such a contract should be

iron-clad and 'not occasionally broken, but should be the law of practice in general.

While it is most desirable to derive pleasure from the act, *there must be a deeper and more holy object in view.* In the process of REgeneration there is no actual waste of vital force *if* the Rite is completed. If the embrace is indulged for any other purpose than generation, there should be *a full understanding between them to concentrate on some holy object or lofty ideal.* There must be harmony between them and the crisis of both should occur as nearly as possible at the same time. The thought and the desire should be intensely held at the moment and it is well to draw up the breath and hold it during the exchange of the vital forces.

If this is faithfully performed the vital energy in the seminal fluid will be absorbed by the intensity of the female orgasm and will electrify her entire body, just as the electric current charges the bar of steel that has previously been prepared for a magnet.

In the male the thought and retained breath will absorb the magnetic force in the *lochia* released by the glands of the vagina and uterus. We repeat, there is no waste; but a fair exchange which is resultant of peace, happiness and health[1].

There are very few people, irrespective whether married or single, who actually understand sexual laws; consequently it is rarely that the embrace is consummated as it should be. In most instances he indulges with no thought beyond his immediate gratification, receiving neither joy nor strength; hence little wonder she comes to hate and despise the act and

---

[1] Let *wise* men and fools sneer all they please. Here is a *mystery* for happiness and the means to race REgeneration. It is the *other,* the *spiritual side* of sex.

feels disgust at the mere thought of it. Because of this ignorance and selfishness the exercise is hardly ever performed in a divine and holy manner but becomes a purely mechanical matter-of-fact, uninspired process. Here, indeed, is one of the main causes for much of the dissatisfaction in married life.

If a man does not love a woman to the extent of wanting to caress and kiss her *before* he indulges in the Rite, and to do so *after* the completion of the embrace, he does not really love her; the most that can be said for him is, that he is impassioned by her. Under such conditions he has no right to request her favors; to do so is to prostitute his powers and energies.

The lover's kiss, like the creative exercise, has been much misunderstood and abused. It is as sacred in the sight of God as the marriage Rite. The kiss is the symbol of true love, an emblem of affection; or, *it may be the badge of hypocrisy*—the kiss of Judas. It is sanctioned only between those who love each other, between women who are good friends, and between relatives. Any other indulgence is hypocritical and degrading to those kissing. On this basis it should be readily understandable how undesirable it must be in instances where the kiss is exchanged between those who dislike each other, aye, even come to hate each other.

Women are most frequently the lawbreakers. Who has not observed women kissing each other even when known to be bitter enemies? This is comparable to the famous Biblical kiss of Judas.

Another cause for the cooling of affection and what was once intense love may in some instances depend on temperamental differences, or can be traced to the general practice of continually sharing one bed. The married should sometimes occupy separate beds, and, when possible to arrange, often separate rooms, that modesty and privacy may be respected. The freedom often displayed in dressing and undressing in one another's presence is seldom conducive to the greatest attractiveness for one another, or deepest respect.

Those who live the manner of married life indicated will not be prudes; nor see anything in sex of which to be ashamed. To them all that pertains to the creative function will be beautiful, holy, divine, a special blessing and privilege which a considerate God conferred upon his children. They will also recognize that there is a time and a place for all things.

There are periods when he intensely wishes to see the beautiful outlines of the feminine form, and actually longs to "raise the veil," just as there are times when *she desires* him to do this. If they always share the same room and the one bed, the "human form divine" may become too common a sight; leaving nothing to the imagination of the god Love. Once imagination is dead, love quickly follows in the wake of the funeral.

Our experience teaches us that all who believe that sex is only for the gratification of the senses, who over-indulge and seldom, if ever, know a perfect union, having prostituted, debased and debauched the generative energy and so became abnormal, cannot see anything beautiful or divine in God's simple, yet most mysterious part of creation. The happily married are far removed from these unfortunates.

Too often those entering the marital relationship become careless in dress and appearance. Both should continually strive to please each other in this respect, after, as before the ringing of the wedding bells. When a woman becomes careless of her appearance, the husband's imagination may grow wayward and envisage a different woman than the one constantly appearing before him.

The reaction, of disillusionment—for that's what it amounts to — has the tendency to cool the depth of his love for her. Woman is not alone guilty. Indeed, the man frequently becomes more careless than she. Before marriage, he was a man in every respect; neat in appearance; gentlemanly in deportment; kindly, considerate, affectionate. To continue in this manner, after marriage, may seem too much trouble, but he must realize that her love means his happiness and he should exert every effort to retain it.

Love is the sum total of woman's life. Man is indeed foolish if he attempts to change her attitude. There never can be any "settling down" in her case. She expects the days of courtship in one form or another to continue *after* the wedding ceremony. Those little favors, flowers, presents, pleasing speeches and little flatteries are always desired by the *real* woman. All of them are a part of her being.

Irrespective of how prosaic or practical life may be, how many sorrows may be her share, these little attentions are as ointment to wounds; together they comprise the foundation of her continued love for him. He should gladly and freely perform these gentlemanly considerations, and never with the feeling or attitude that they are arduous tasks.

The young wife, on her part, should constantly remember that with man conditions differ. He draws a line of distinction between love, passion and business. Business is cold, calculating, and without emotion; foreign to a woman's nature.

Whatever a woman becomes interested in is based upon

the emotion of either love or hate. She must never for a moment permit herself to forget that *man can completely divorce passion from love.* He can actually have passion for a woman without feeling any love for her, though he is not master enough to love a woman for whom he cannot feel passion.

In woman's sphere, except in rare cases, this is entirely different. Although she may be passionate, she will seldom allow her desires to be aroused unless she loves. Men and women are distinctly different from each other in their affectional natures. To obtain happiness and avoid grievous mistakes which often lead to sorrow and unhappiness, each must not judge the other by *his or her own nature.*

Dr. P. B. Randolph, often termed the world's greatest philosopher of love, stated it as a law, that woman will forgive a man if he so far forgets himself as to have sexual congress with another woman, but will never pardon him if she learns he has been caressing, kissing, and loving her, because this would be an affront to her own affectional nature, the *law* of her existence.

On the contrary, a man may forgive his wife when guilty of infatuation for another man, but will never do so if he knows her to be guilty of sexual embrace with another; because the very basis of his being and his deepest love is founded in passion, which he considers sacred and holy unto himself alone.

Another important truth which should be instilled into every young man, one he should never forget under penalty of forever losing the respect of a true woman who may love him, is this: Never, or under any circumstances in her presence, voice any coarse, common or slighting comment on her sex, or any function of woman.

If she is true-hearted and loving, and we are considering only such, she expects, and rightly so, that he is a gentleman and considers every part of her being and of woman generally, as beautiful and desirable. If ever he foolishly attempts any slighting allusion, no matter what the motive, to her creative organism, or any other part of her body, especially of her breasts, she will be so deeply wounded that she will rarely, if ever, fully recover and again evince her former love for him.

The case of a little woman coming to us suffering from extreme nervousness, will partly illustrate this. We were well acquainted with both the young people before their marriage. She was a jolly little girl, a good companion, carefree and lovable. He was quite serious and apparently ignorant of the little weaknesses which make women lovable. They were married; and for a time, happy.

After the birth of the first child, she lost some of her plumpness, especially the roundness of her breasts. On one occasion, just before the embrace, he foolishly made the remark that he did not like the appearance of her breasts as well as he did before they were married.

This cut her to the quick, causing her to brood over her loss, and inducing her to try every means in her power to regain her former symmetry, but all to no avail. The continual nursing of the wounded feelings finally resulted in a nervous ailment lasting for years and the expenditure of much money.

After consulting many physicians without relief, (and it must be here mentioned, he loved her deeply enough to make every effort to find relief for her), she came to us, confessing the cause of all her trouble. It required some little time and effort to convince her that merely because he had foolishly told her he liked her better, or preferred her with her former appearance, did not in the least imply that he loved her less the way she now was. She was told that, as an actual truth, he might even love her more when in this plight, because of his sympathy.

What a man "likes" and what he actually "loves" are two entirely different things. This is readily shown by the self-evident fact that a man likes to see his wife well and strong, but may dearly love her even though she is seriously ill. Once fully convinced of her erroneous interpretation of his remark, she made every effort to forget the incident, and within a few months was entirely free of the nervous affliction, and was her happy self again.

Some will question: "Does this mean that a man must be constantly on his guard in order to retain his sweetheart's or wife's deepest affection?"

We counter by another question: Must not the true musician FOREVER be on guard that he does not strike the wrong note?

An important question frequently asked: "How often should the marital embrace be indulged in?" There is no answer to this question. It depends first of all on the temperaments of those asking the question; on the state of mind and body, on their vitality and virility, on their age and on many other factors. If both are about equally sexed, then there should be an understanding and agreement not to engage in the Rite so frequently as to cause a feeling of weakness or enervation. The Rite correctly indulged in should always result in a feeling of peace and well-being. If one is highly sexed while the other is more or less sexually cool, then there must be an understanding and patience one with the other, each one conceding both the rights and abilities of the other; one not demanding too much, the other not refusing too much. In all cases, understanding and compromise alone can be the foundation of both satisfaction and happiness.

There are well-defined indications of the right use of sex laws which, if observed and followed, will give the correct answer to every questioner. So long as the embrace is exercised by two people who love each other, and a feeling of well-being and joyousness, without a hint of shamefulness, is resultant, it is a clear and unmistakable indication that there has been no over-indulgence. When the man feels equal to the day's task and is enabled to do it easily and cheerfully, when the woman finds it a joy and satisfaction to perform her duties, and her labor does not seem in the nature of drudgery, then normality is clearly evidenced. Under such conditions, the act is an incentive.

The man and woman whose present, and future, welfare signifies more to them than the immediate pleasure of indulgence, will regulate their conduct in this respect. The slightest hint of weakness or lassitude should be accepted as a warning; an indication of over-indulgence, a warning that the frequency of the embrace must be reduced. When good results follow a stated regime, the parties concerned are justified in believing that all is as it should be. In general, young married people should agree to certain elastic rules and regulations governing the exercise and adhere to them. Three times a week is usually a safe and sane rule to abide by.

PREPARING FOR THE BABY

"That Which is Worth Doing is Worth Doing Well"

LL of us are familiar with the old maxim, but how few of us are actually governed by it in our actions! This precept is most emphatically applicable to the important subject now under consideration, but should be made even more positive: "If a child is to be born it has a *right* to be *born well*."

God's greatest and most sublimely mysterious gift to man is the power of procreation. Very few of the teeming millions ever give this truth even a serious thought. This is in great part due to the fact that the creation of the human species is almost without exception an accident—an undesired by-product of an impassioned moment—rather than what it should really be, a planned result of a sacred marital Rite.

Up to the present, except in rare instances, Nature has had the entire responsibility placed upon her by an ignorant and selfish humanity. Now that the Laws of Heredity and Pre-natal influences[1] are becoming generally known, and since the *Law of Personal Responsibility for all our acts is being taught,* men and women *should carefully consider the results* before engaging in an act which is NEVER NEUTRAL, but always is, or becomes, either a blessing or a curse upon all concerned.

The Laws of Heredity deal with the inheritance of the good or evil qualities native to the parents, and which may have

---

[1] See *The Creation of a Perfect Baby* by *Prenatal Culture,* Philosophical Publishing Company, Quakertown, Penna.

been transmitted to them by their parents, grand parents, or even great-grand parents.

The Laws of Prenatal influence, on the other hand, govern the impressions made directly upon the child by the parents, especially the mother, of qualities, powers, potentialities and capabilities, as also virtues and vices not native to the parents, but which they have the power to direct to the child. It can be readily understood that generally Prenatal influences have a much wider field of influence and are of far greater importance than Heredity.

Many scientific men ridicule the possibility of investing the unborn with powers and virtues not possessed by the parents. We maintain that the mother can give birth to a superior being by surrounding herself with works of art, beautiful paintings, and objects which elevate the thoughts, and by gazing upon them often, meanwhile concentrating her desires on impressing the child in her bosom with loftiness of mind, strength and beauty of physique, and greatness of Soul.

Though scientists smile at the simplicity of minds having faith in the power for good of such impressions on the unborn, we seriously question whether they would allow us to display at the foot of the bed wherein slept their wives when *enceinte,* pictures depicting fearful accidents, the carnage of war, or of men with misshapen bodies or ugly countenance.

We feel certain that they would not permit this. They would admit to us that such pictures were potent to affect the mind and nerves of the mothers, and perhaps indirectly or directly the well-being of the unborn.

To this we also agree, though we question in all sincerity the reason they base their claim that pictures depicting undesirable scenes and misshapen personalities have the power to influence conscious and unconscious minds, while they deny the force of the beautiful and aesthetic to impress for good the mother-to-be and her child. The laws governing the incentives and actions of Life are dual, not single or unbalanced.

One of the most simple and authoritative accounts of pre-natal influence or maternal impressions, is given in the Biblical account of Jacob and the sheep.—*Gen.* 31: 37-40

In this it is clearly indicated that even the animal nature is sufficiently impressible so that colors and types may be produced almost at will.

If the truths of these Biblical narratives are admitted, is anyone, scientist or philosopher, irrational enough to claim that the nature of woman, whose nervous system is the finest and most delicate of all creation, is less impressionable and responsive to the beautiful than the animal? *Au contraire,* if scientist and philosopher deny the Biblical record, then they must likewise question every other statement in the Bible.

In the present scientific age we give every consideration to animal husbandry. We carefully study their characteristics and temperament. We seek to know what they like or dislike. We give attention to the question of food, withholding from them what they do not like, and supplying them with what they prefer.

When we mate them we are most careful in the selection of the sire and we remove everything from their presence which seems to in the least irritate them. We *know from experience* that all these things have a powerful influence on both the mature animal and the unborn.

How has it been in the great, mysterious, sublime realm of human creation? Have we given study to the time when conception should properly take place? Have we taught humanity the right season for the propagation of the species? Have we made a study of the proper preparation for the conceiving mother? Have we taught womanhood generally when this should occur?

Have we studied the great problem of proper diet, and have we taught people generally the sane conclusions reached? Have we studied the impressions of the beautiful on woman's mental and nervous systems during the period of pregnancy? Have we watched the effects of the ugly and undesirable, and taught her what to avoid, or, that failing, how to overcome these depressing influences? Have we taught the feminine world the serious consequences of reading exciting or morbid literature during the period of pregnancy?

Have we been thorough in our researches and willingly offered to all the fruits of our labors, or have we complacently allowed all the details of birth and child-bearing to take care of themselves, thus unthinkingly contributing our bit to the weakness and degradation of present and future generations? Can we expect Nature to produce a god, while supplying her with the material and opportunity unsuited even to the creation of an idiot?

Men and women have not as yet awakened to even a partial comprehension of the potentialities with which Nature has endowed them. They have not become conscious of their great responsibilities, duties and possibilities in the creative sphere. Thus far every thought has been of themselves, their own salvation; the idea never entering their minds that not alone are they held responsible by God's great Law for their own welfare, but likewise accountable for that of their children, their children's children, and even their great-grandchildren.

Mothers and fathers must quickly awaken to their *rights* and their *responsibilities.* There is a sinister movement rapidly taking form, the intentions of which are undoubtedly commendable; but it is leading the race towards the

Shoals Ahead

There are certain groups of "busy-bodies" quietly making plans to disrupt family life as we know it. For the most part this group is composed of women who have never been mothers; have not the slightest idea of what the feeling of motherhood would be; and of men who have thus far refused to accept the responsibility of fatherhood. Their idea is the formation of a department of public welfare, plus the enactment of laws governing the instruction and training of the children.

So far, well and good, but the ulterior object of this movement is to take from the *bona fide* mothers and fathers throughout the land, *the control and training, the intellectual, and even the spiritual direction of the children.*

In Sparta of old this was actually accomplished—*that nation is now known only in name.* In foreign countries such efforts are more or less successful, if we so consider totalitarianism—man, the creature of the State.

> We foresee that when this is actually attempted in America, the entire *motherhood will arise in their might as one; the governing power sanctioning it will be swept aside as a straw in the wind, and the deluded men and women who select themselves to wrest the child from its rightful mother, will thereby seal their own doom.*

God's greatest blessing, as also His greatest privilege, is

sacred motherhood. It is our duty to study the problem and teach mothers and mothers-to-be. No unmarried man or woman, shirking the responsibility of parenthood, has any moral or spiritual right to disrupt the harmony, desires or activity of a family.

The problem of Heredity must have our careful consideration. We must instruct both men and women in its influence on the unborn. This we can best do by concrete examples.

In 1909 the Physio-Medical Society of the State of Indiana held its convention at Indianapolis. During one of the sessions, a carefully prepared paper dealing with the problem of Heredity was read by one of the members of the Society.

It appears there lived in the western part of Pennsylvania, a family then little known, but later to become extremely notorious. To this family was born a girl, more or less mentally weak[2] and as usual at the time, even as at the present, with the exception of feeding and clothing her, she had little attention, no instruction or training, and no one to guard her against evil.

This girl, ignorant, unprepared, and unprotected, was betrayed by a male brute with the usual result: a female child was born to her.

The parents, instead of doing their duty and exercising every effort in their power that neither she nor her child should become the victims of other such renegades, cast both of them on the public welfare. Neither society nor State had the slightest inclination to look after the outcasts, with the

---

[2]Today, with our knowledge of the functioning of the ductless glands and of Endocrinology in the treatment of diseases, especially mental weaknesses in children, almost all of such ailments in children respond to treatment, with the result that mental health is completely restored.

result that they were the beginning of a long line of degenerate men and women. The record, as given, was this:

"Sixty members of the descendants had court records, fifteen had been in jail, fourteen in the penitentiary, nine in the infirmary, nine in children's homes, six in the workhouse, two in the Girls' Industrial Home, two in the Institution for Feeble-minded, and one in the Boys' Industrial Home.

"Seventy-seven were immoral, seventy-four criminal in varying degrees, fifty-five feeble-minded, twenty-three alcoholics, twelve public women, seven tubercular, six children adopted into homes, four epileptics, three insane, and three wanderers who labored not.

"Among the crimes of which some of these were guilty, we find catalogued: burglary, forgery, destruction of property, owners or inmates of immoral houses, intoxication, rioting, perjury, various degenerating practices, homicide, and poisoning with intent to kill.

"The mentality of the adult degenerate members of the family was that of children between seven and twelve years."

Who really was the guilty party? Where does the actual blame belong? Was the poor victim, through whose ignorance this long line of degenerates had its beginning, alone to bear the penalty?

We maintain she was the least to blame. Conceived in ignorance, poorly born, receiving neither instructions nor training, *such as should have been hers by right of having been born,* she followed Nature's inclination in doing what she did.

Her spiritual nature was completely submerged and unawakened, hence totally failing her in all her needs. Will God hold her responsible, society as a whole having failed her?

Such a picture of the shortcomings of the individual and society, plus the results following, is certainly not a pleasant one. It illustrates many other experiences of like nature. We exempt this woman from blame because of her ignorance and weakness, but we cannot hold the modern woman blameless because she has every opportunity to gain full knowledge of the laws governing the creative function and the rightful, constructive use of this great gift and capacity with which the Creator has endowed her.

It is easily possible for any woman of ordinary intelligence to become the mother of a race of mental, physical, spiritual giants, of mental and spiritual masters.

How?

By instructing her in all the duties she owes to herself as a woman and to the race having its beginning with her. She can be taught to think constructively and gloriously; to study helpful instructive books; to select the foods for their body-building and health-giving value. She can be carefully taught exercises that will develop the mind, the Will and her entire physical being. She can acquaint herself with the Laws which will enable her to "build" an outstanding new temple for the reception of a Soul, directly from "heaven."

Such a woman will love both well and wisely. She will marry. She will see to it that the creative forces are not dissipated or, in Biblical terms, "cast upon the ground" to damn her and her progeny, and she will, in due and proper time, conceive. She will study the books she is assured will have an elevating and constructive influence on the mind of both herself and the child later to be born, be it boy or girl.

She will not permit obscene or suggestive pictures in the house, nor attend plays or movies which are suggestive, degrading or debasing. She will associate only with cultured people who use chaste language. She will be careful when bathing; taking cold baths for stimulation; warm baths for cleanliness and relaxation.

She will follow a system of physical exercise and breathing drills; keep fully and interestingly occupied, and avoid everything that might possibly be nerve-shocking or that would tend to induce hysteria.

Above all, she is careful in the selection of her diet, avoiding all articles of food that could possibly congest the system or interfere with good circulation and a clear brain.

She refuses marital relationship with her husband unless first brought to a keen desire by his caresses; she is sufficiently unshackled mentally, and woman enough to indicate her real feelings when her wedded partner fails to notice them.

Let a woman thus trained, and living such a life, conceive, impress, and give birth to a child, and it will mark the beginning of a REgenerate Race.

Let us suppose this child to be a girl. The mother instructs her in the truth as she was taught; trains her under all the laws governing the development of her true womanhood. This child, on reaching adolescence, then motherhood, in her turn teaches and develops her children in like manner. Can we even begin to estimate what this will mean to the nation within a few generations? We can, however, form some conception of the influence such superior men and women would have on the affairs of nations, their morals being uncorruptible.

It cannot be successfully argued that this is purely a dream of an ideal state, impractical in every day life. Men and women *can* obtain good literature as readily as destructive, vulgar, and obscene publications. They need have no greater difficulty in securing beautiful pictures than those depicting destruction or vulgarity. They can keep mind and body occupied instead of catering to their "nerves"; can walk and exercise in place of lounging about the house or club; and have the choice of attending good plays and operas instead of choosing questionable shows. What is even more important, they can obtain good, nutritious, nerve and brain building foods as cheaply as rich meats, sweets, cookies, candies, spiced articles and useless desserts having no actual value to the body, but clogging the entire eliminative system, producing weakness and low mental states.

A sane, sensible, purposeful life is no more difficult to live than is a destructive, aimless existence. It is merely a question of choice. Just as many are perfectly satisfied to live in an old, leaky, ramshackle hovel, though having the opportunity to move into a modern, sanitary, well-appointed dwelling, so the majority prefer the old, irresponsible, destructive, negative life. The creative life requires no self-denial, merely the desire and determination to do the right thing in the right way, in the right place and at the right time. It forbids no innocent pleasure, no harmless recreation, no good food, nor any enjoyment that contributes to well-being and peace of mind.

Man boasts of being the "lord of creation," but consider his consistency for a moment.

The farmer who masters his vocation studies the requirements of his soil; builds it up where it is deficient; plows and carefully prepares his fields. When the time arrives, he patronizes a dealer in whom he has full confidence and selects only the choicest of seeds; those having been tested for germination. He gives strict attention to the proper time for the sowing, choosing days he believes best for the purpose, always having in mind the germination of the seeds.

After the seed has been planted, he gives all the care and cultivation necessary to assure a crop equalling his expectation, and if possible, to improve over the seed sown. And for what? That he may be supplied with food for the winter, or for conversion into money to obtain the pleasures or the necessities of life.

Now give a thought to the propagators of the greatest of all "crops"—the human family. How many make a sincere effort to become fully conversant with the laws governing the functions of creation; how and when the "sowing" should take place; the preparation essential for success? How many give thought that the "seed" is not only fertile, but virile, so that the "stock" be sound and healthy; the "ground" be properly prepared by genuine affection and all that is part of it? How many are vigilant during the period when the "seed" is taking the shape of a new being?

The number, unfortunately for the race, is all too few. To the vast majority procreation is merely an incident. All too frequently it is an accident, and when it does "happen," the parents let Nature look after her own labors.

Moreover, in all too many instances, at least the "he" of the twain would rather that the seed did not find fertile ground and germinate; moreover, he does all in his power, and *not* always in any natural way, to prevent it.

If, despite all efforts, conception does take place under such conditions and circumstances, the child so unholily conceived is born with an inheritance of weakness, possibly with criminal tendencies; frequently ill, a source of sorrow instead of happiness. Then the un-comprehending parents unbless God for visiting such misfortune upon them, wholly ignorant and unconscious of their own criminality.

If we desire strong, healthy, superior babies, we must go back a step beyond consideration of the Laws of Heredity and Pre-natal influences. We must begin with the children already born, carefully instructing them in all the Laws of Procreation, preparing them for the great work before them, and thoroughly training them to eradicate all that is weak and undesirable— all this before they have even reached the age of responsibility.

We must carefully and thoroughly instruct them in all the laws pertaining to environments, imitation, personal and Pre-natal influences, and Heredity, that they may employ all of this knowledge when they become co-creators with God. We must impress upon them the necessity of thorough preparation; that this is half the battle; that while Heredity is the foundation, Pre-natal influences and impressions are the building; one is quite as important as the other.

Is this labor worth the effort? While we are in youth and the world looks bright and rosy, we have no little loved ones of our own whose suffering we must witness. As we advance in years, many little feet cross our path, some of them our own, and as we see their suffering and are helpless to relieve it, we begin to appreciate the vast importance of doing our best to either prevent, or at least to partially minimize this misery and sorrow, rather than merely seeking a remedy for temporary relief.

The fearful price paid for the heedless and senseless fashion in which our children are conceived, born and reared, is readily understood when we bear in mind that, for instance, in the United States, a nation highly favored in all things, there are now several millions of weaklings and degenerates filling prisons and other institutions. This vast multitude does not include the countless army suffering from advanced stages of syphilis and other immoral diseases resulting from depraved practices by the debased and degenerate.

In no department of creation or reproduction is man so grossly ignorant or neglectful as in that of the conception, the birth and the development of his children, despite the fact that no where else is to be found the source of so much real joy and happiness. Moreover, man willfully and skillfully avoids the subject as though it were of the least concern to him. The awful penalty mankind has paid because of ignorance and indifference lo, these many centuries, has failed to awaken him to both his possibilities and his responsibilities.

How strangely true it is that there are "none so blind as those who will not see."

THE LAW OF TRANSMISSION

HEREDITY

O ONE is in a better position to explain and prove the Law of Transmission, usually termed Heredity, than the experienced breeder of pedigreed stock. With him there is no such thing as chance. Every animal has its history and none are afforded the opportunity to breed indiscriminately.

When he mates "Gypsy" or "Beverly" to "Bonita, the third," he has detailed information before him covering both the weak and strong points possessed by each, and confidently expects certain characteristics to dominate in the young of the pair. If these should be missing, if weakness or other defects are present, he must seek for the cause in the care of the female during the period of gestation, or attribute it to a "throwback" of several generations.

In considering the law of transmission with relation to its influence on the human species, we must recognize that heredity governs only in part, being modified by so many factors that the Law itself hardly ever has the opportunity to work out fully or naturally. The every-day life, behavior and mental influence of the mother all having profound effects on her offspring.

In animal husbandry we have no such influences to consider. The animal has no "mental attitude." It is not given to moods, tantrums, violent hatreds, resentments, emotional upsets, or what not, all of which have a powerful influence upon the

physical self of the mother-to-be, her spiritual self and, indirectly, upon the child in gestation. The animal is mated as
wisely as humanly possible. At the correct time, after the
female conceives, the male is non-existent to her and Heredity
or the Law of Mendel governs from then on until the young
are born.

Mating and the bearing of young in the animal kingdom
are governed by natural law; the owner merely selects mates
best suited to each other and to offset or eliminate weaknesses.

We learn most readily by illustration, and to serve the
purpose of illustration here, we draw on our past experience.
For more than ten years we experimented in the breeding of
fancy poultry, and five years were devoted to raising pedigreed
Collies.

For a female short in head and weak in coat, we selected for
service a male lengthy of head with heavy coat. By this
process we expected the male to transmit to the young his
heaviness of coat as well as greater length of head. However,
admittedly, we were confronted with the *great unknown:*
which of the mating pair possessed the greater transmitability?

If the female happens to be more virile than the male,
then it is altogether possible for her to transmit to the young
her own characteristics and this would naturally cause her
young to be much like herself. At the same time, despite
the potency of her greater vitality, we still expect heavier
coats for the young than she possesses, because vitality is one
of the factors needed to produce a heavy coat.

If the male possessed the greater vitality, then we confidently looked forward to puppies with long heads; but
even here unknown laws often govern, and some characteristics
of a former generation may manifest.

This law can be even more clearly illustrated. There are several distinct types of Collies. The one most commonly known is the Sable and White; next the Tricolor, usually black, sable and white—being black of body, with white markings and sable around the eyes and possibly the mouth; lastly, the Blue Merle.

By mating a pair of Sable and White we would naturally look for young of the same color, with perhaps some modification of the tint. But there is no certainty; it is altogether possible that out of a litter of six healthy pups, five will be Sable and White, while the sixth may be a Tricolor, or even a black. What is the explanation for such an occurrence?

It merely indicates that, several generations back, one of the ancestors, either of the male or female, was a Tricolor, and that in the blood of one of the present parents there still remain some of the blood cells of this fore-parent.

Thus we have a "throw-back" or reversion of type. This impregnation of a cell of a former generation is identical to the transmission from parent to child of a disease, such as syphilis; though the transmitter is apparently not in the least afflicted with it. Of this we will speak later.

If a pair of fairly evenly matched Collies are mated, let us say of the desired length of head, heaviness of coat, and strength of bone; *not too closely related;* if the care and the food of the female is as it should be, we may confidently expect the young to possess the features of the parents; healthy and strong, and of like color.

Such a rule does not always govern the human family. If the parents are too much alike in features, temperaments and other characteristics, even though not at all related, the children resulting from the union, if any, may be the direct opposite of parents.

In the human family, the rule generally governing is: "Like produces like." If the parents are equal, in vitality, or nearly so, the likeness is more frequently after the mother rather than the father. This is for the reason that, while the father supplies the seed of life, and all of the future human monad is contained in this Spermatozoon, including the basis for health or the inoculation of an inherited disease, as the case may be, it is the mother who, during the period of gestation, fashions the new being by her mental attitude and mode of life in general. The thoughts of her mind, the passions of her entire being, and the emotions of her heart, profoundly impress the being in the process of creation.

If the mother-to-be is fully enlightened in the Creative Law, she is enabled to bring forth a god-man, a superior being, even though the father is practically a nonentity. Her work can extend to giving the child a healthy body and powerful virility, though the father is a weakling, provided, of course, that his blood is not filled with germs of syphilis or other transmittable disease, and his nerves and brain untainted with insanity.

We modify this last statement and claim that even these— cancer and syphilis—can be eliminated by the mother during the time of gestation.

Although we have made the statement that most frequently the child favored the mother, we do not wish to be understood as maintaining that this is always so. A superior man wedded to an honest, lovable, but inferior woman is enabled to father a genius by obedience to the law following.

The period during which man possesses the greatest creative potency is while he most desires the marital embrace; is filled with and manifests affection and love. It is at such moments that he concentrates every force within his being, and if the marital Rite is consummated at this time, he is, at the moment of the climax, thoroughly positive in every department of his little world.

If the woman granted his request after being thoroughly awakened to desire through endearments, giving him her love, and if he, during the entire embrace, especially at the moment of highest bliss, concentrates his mind on the one object of calling into existence a healthy, normal, and superior child, *he is enabled to draw the potential forces from Heaven itself.* This longing, hurled into space, will become a part of the child to be.

He is enabled to still further influence the health, strength and character of the coming child, by at each embrace concentrating all his energies toward that objective, thereby charging the vital fluids given to, and absorbed by, the mother-to-be; helping her to build body, nerve and brain into the new creation.

When both man and woman understand this one secret of Race REgeneration, the propagation of healthy, normal, natural and God-like offspring will be much more certain. We venture to say that ten wedded couples who truly love and have full comprehension of the law, faithfully practicing its tenets, could completely revolutionize this old world; their progeny would be so positive, so virile and influential, as to enable them to beneficially rule the races.

While the mother's influence is naturally much greater in fashioning the character and features of the child than is the father's, she cannot so readily inoculate it with such a disease as syphilis. When diseases are transmitted by the father the transmission occurs through the life germ in the seminal fluid. When this takes place it is not always an indication that *he is* diseased, because it is entirely possible that his father, or grand-father, or even great-grandfather, may have been the sufferer and the germs, transmitted from generation to generation, have been dormant up to the time they became part of the new creation.

While various diseases are usually inherited from the father, mental conditions, especially insanity and neurotic tendencies, are most frequently impressed or absorbed from the mother, every state of her mind having a pronounced influence upon that of the unborn; it therefore behooves her to be extremely care-ful of her mental attitude while *enceinte.*

Another reason children most frequently favor the mother, all other things being equal, is, that while procreation is a pass-ing fancy or an accident on the part of the father, it absorbs all life of the mother; her energies, thoughts and desires are concentrated on the task before her; consequently she contin-ually impresses her personality, with its likes and dislikes, upon the creation being formed within her bosom.

When we leave the boundary of the physical and enter the realms of the purely mental, we meet with apparently serious contradictions relative to the Law of Heredity. For instance, it is generally known that most of the sons of great men are seldom an honor to their fathers; while those of financial giants are hardly ever successful. At a first superficial glance this would indicate a contradiction of the law; actually it is not.

A man may once have been a physical giant and, while the possessor of such strength, could undoubtedly have fathered an equally potent progeny. Gradually, through abuse or negli-gence, he deteriorates into a weakling, yet remaining capable of procreation. His offspring at this period would hardly be comparable to those fathered in his former virile condition.

For an almost similar reason the great philosopher, victorious general, or powerful magnate, seldom becomes the father of sons and daughters comparable to him; *because his whole mind and all his energies are utilized in the special labor in which he is engaged, and there remains little strength or potency for procreation; in fact, these are generally no more than "by-products."* As a fact, he may be hardly aware of his indulgence, embracing his partner possibly because he considers it his duty; at her instigation; or at the urge of a temporary sensual desire; *very seldom, if ever,* because he longs to call into being one like unto himself. Procreation, with great or successful men, is usually an accident, one for which both they and their progeny suffer deeply.

Let the man who has achieved honor and distinction by reason of his talents set aside his vocation or avocation for a time, husband all his forces and energies, both mental and physical, and then concentrate them all in one Holy Act of Creation, governed by deep affection and a thorough preparation of his mate, and the world will be astonished at the result, while he and the Great Creator will be glorified.

Although Heredity undoubtedly underlies our strength and our weakness, it should not serve as an excuse for any undesirable inheritance we possess. Any one not physically or mentally all he should be, or would like to be, should be too much of a *man* or *woman* to place the blame on being thus born.

The inheritance of a weak body does not give man the slightest excuse for remaining weak during all of a lifetime; experience daily indicates that many of the really great statesmen, athletes, and philosophers, as well as others who have won world renown, were not born with any great physical strength, mental power, or financial backing, but obtained all of these through a refusal to bow the knee to fate, and by personal effort on their part, removed every obstacle and undesirable quality.

Similarly, because a man inherits syphilis from, or through one of his parents, is no legitimate excuse for him to remain a victim of this filthy, degrading and degenerating disease throughout his entire life and to die from it while still in youth. He is able, through force of Will, cleanliness and saneness of life and proper treatment, to eradicate it from his system; becoming as undefiled as if neither his parents nor he himself had ever been contaminated with it.

We should fully recognize the force of the Law of Transmission; but it is likewise our indisputable duty to seek understanding of the greater Law: *That we are what we make of ourselves.* That we are a combination of how we live, the food we eat, the thoughts we think, the desires we harbor, and our efforts to overcome or succeed.

Unquestionably, a powerful mental effort is required to enable those born weak to gain strength and then begin a life potential for accomplishment. The Law of Heredity should not greatly concern those already born; these should search themselves and find their weakness or incompetency, then overcome it. Rather, we should seriously give our consideration to the Law of Transmission.

This law concerns the unborn, and we should recognize and accept our duty to enlighten the world of its power to influence the physical, mental and spiritual welfare of those yet to be born; that these may not be burdened with the weaknesses and vices that curse the multitudes.

Humanity should be taught, as the sacred duty of our present civilization, not to indulge in the marital rite during periods when conception may take place, unless this is desired and they themselves are physically and mentally fit. To reason by analogy: the wise man will not attempt the construction of a house until he has prepared a sound foundation and is prepared to furnish all the material, so that when finished, it may be the "mansion of his dreams." On this same basis, conception should not be made possible until full preparation has been made for the purpose.

After conception does occur, the parents have definite duties to perform. Self-government on the part of each is of the greatest importance. The marital embrace should be undertaken only in its highest aspect, love and affection, not with mere passion as the incentive. The husband should never attempt to force his attention on the wife, but should arouse her to desire by fondling and caressing. She on her part should respond unless there are good reasons for her not to do so.

When the embrace is undertaken it must not be discontinued until her conjugal love is fully requited. The frequency of the embrace must depend altogether on the mother-to-be, though it is well for her to prevent frigidity or too great passion in herself. It is equally important for the husband to understand that if the mother-to-be courts the embrace and is refused, the child may be born love hungry, a Magdalene, through no fault of her own.

These are a few of the important considerations in the procreation of a new entity. Admittedly, under present conditions the average husband has no understanding of the law; is governed by his carnal desires; disgusts his mate by his inconsideration, and thus forever impresses the child with like aversion; damning it through all the days of its life; creating in its nature desires ending in perversions, or frigidity and utter absence of feeling.

On the contrary, if the father labors under the erroneous belief that it is wrong to have sexual congress with the mother while *enceinte,* and she suffers from love hunger during this period, the child is almost certain to be impressed with this craving all its life, manifesting it by being unhappy in the companionship of one man or one woman; forever seeking, but never satisfied.

The mother-to-be has equally a duty to the unborn. She must govern her mental attitude to avoid impressing the child with impatience, hysteria, or the many other emotions resulting from an unsettled mind. She must build up the body by proper food, bathing and exercise, elevating her mental forces by right thinking, cheerfulness, chaste thoughts, the reading of good books, listening to good music, and the indulgence in healthful and wholesome recreations. A mother's duty is tremendous. If she fulfills it, however, she will be compensated a thousand-fold; the love she harbors in her heart and mind for the unborn will be the connecting link binding the child to her and to God in the years to come.

Many women develop a strange and apparently unreasonable appetite during the period of gestation. If this is for something which is in itself harmful, it should not be satisfied, but something of benefit substituted. If the appetite or desire is not harmful to her health and well-being, it should be supplied as quickly as possible to avoid unpleasant or undesirable physical disturbances.

Irrespective of the opinions of the mother-to-be on the subject of morality, she should not read salacious literature. Under no circumstances should she engage in conversation that is unchaste, because of the impressions on her mind and emotions; nor should she associate with individuals of questionable character. She should make every effort to elevate her thoughts, desires and inclinations toward all that is good and constructive. Irrespective of opinions to the contrary, every passion, appetite, desire and emotion of the mother-to-be is impressed upon the spiritual nature of the child during gestation. These are *felt* by the mother-to-be and all *feelings* are impressed upon the Soul. *This is the Law underlying Race Regeneration.*

Recommendations: Conception should be planned; never the result of an "accident" in the satisfaction of gross passions. Prior thereto, both husband and wife, and especially the wife, should consult the family physician for a thorough physical check-up, including blood count, blood pressure, urinary analysis and examination of the heart. If any defect is present, it should first be corrected. If all is well, pregnancy may take place.

Regular examinations *after* pregnancy are of value, but before pregnancy it is a *must* if undue sickness, sorrow and expense is to be avoided. Perfect manhood and womanhood is not the result of one or two things, but of *many* things in proper combination.

DANGEROUS PERIOD OF LIFE

MENOPAUSE

S AT puberty, the temple doors of the creative being are opened so that God's universe may be peopled, so at Menopause are they closed and if all has been well, Nature bespeaks the benediction: "As thou has been faithful despite all thy suffering, now may thou know the joys of life without the shadow of fear."

The period of a woman's fruitful years are varied. In some instances menstruation may commence as early as the age of nine or ten and continue until fifty. In others the lunar season does not appear until the fifteenth or even the eighteenth year, ceasing at thirty-five to thirty-eight.

Many conditions influence both the commencement and the cessation. Heredity frequently governs, and the girl whose mother changed from girlhood to womanhood after reaching the age of fifteen, and from fertility into Menopause at thirty-eight, may expect the same rule to govern in her life, although this is not always true.

Women who have borne children do not usually enter the menopause as early in life as those who have not. As a general rule, the more children a woman has had, the later she may expect the "Change of Life" to occur.

A fallacy which has been universally accepted as a truth, and from which we hope to free suffering womanhood, is the race belief that as a woman approaches the years when menopause should occur, she will commence to suffer all the misery, both physical and mental, that the flesh is heir to.

Nothing need be further from the truth; physical ailments and mental morbidity are not generally necessary, and when present, merely indicate either ignorance or an abnormal life.

At this period of life the creative organism does undergo a change, the ovaries atrophying, reducing in size and ceasing to function as previously. It is also generally believed that the uterus, like the ovaries, will atrophy. No doubt this does occur in some instances, *but it is entirely unnecessary. If the laws governing woman's sexual life and activity are understood and obeyed, women undergoing menopause may remain as youthful in their desires and their capacity to exchange the full love embrace with husbands as before the change, and one of the chief causes of divorces at this period of life — in plain words, the wife's frigidity and lack of response—will have been removed.*

During the period when menopause takes place the entire nervous system must undergo a thorough re-adjustment. One of the first symptoms of the approach of a normal change of life is irregularity in menstruation. Sometimes the lunar flow will be missed for several months. Then it may appear regularly for some time; again ceasing for a shorter or longer period. This continues until the process of reconstruction is completed.

Undoubtedly, even in the strongest women who have lived in obedience with natural laws, the various changes require greater strength than did the monthly periods of cleansing. Because of this, the food should be especially vitalizing and free from congesting material, while the body should have less active exercise and the mind longer hours of rest.

Teaching by illustration is by far the easiest method. We recall the case of an average woman who, during her youth, received no instructions in the care of her physical organism; who refused all oportunities for gaining this important knowledge. She was the mother of several children, suffering severely when giving birth to most of them, by reason of improper food, worry, overwork and many other unnatural and unnecessary factors.

This woman is now in her fourth year of the change. A day or two before the commencement of the flow there is a disturbance of the stomach, then a bilious headache so severe it becomes necessary for her to go to bed. This headache may continue twenty-four to forty-eight hours. During this time she is practically unable to see, so great is her suffering.

Then the flow of an odorous fluid commences and continues for possibly five or six days. The woman is irritable, at times extremely nervous, and next to irrational. From present appearances the change will not be completed for another year or two. Our experience indicates that, with slight variations, this is the usual "hell of middle life" through which most women pass.

We also have in mind an acquaintance, a woman who was blessed with an enlightened mother by whom she was fully instructed during her girlhood years. This lady no longer believes that she need be ashamed of any portion of her body, but feels that she has a perfect right to be proud of it.

She has long since thrown into discard the age-old idea that she is the plaything of her husband, with no right to refuse his request, or indicate her desires; also the belief that when she passes through the gates of the menopause she will no longer be a desirable companion for her husband, and incapable of offering him the pleasures of youth.

This lady, the mother of nine children, at the age of forty-eight, had neither a thought nor an indication of the approaching crisis until the lunar flow ceased to appear. A day or two after the period when menstruation should have commenced she was aware of slightly hot flushes and a desire to rest.

Instead of giving way to worry, *woman's usual companion,* she took a warm douche, a tepid bath with a quick rub, a hot cup of tea and went to bed. In a few hours these flushes passed and she felt wide-awake, though slightly nervous. In place of asking for an opiate, she dressed and took a long walk, swinging her arms and breathing deeply.

For the next few days she changed her diet to luscious fruits and fresh green vegetables, such as lettuce, celery, corn, peas, and plenty of milk and fresh eggs. During the time of what had formerly been the lunar season she abstained from meats, sweets, spices and stimulating drinks.

The next periodical flow appeared as usual, but she continued the former treatment. After an intermittent appearance for about a year, the flow ceased entirely and for six months past there has been no indication of its ever again appearing.

During all of this period she never for a moment permitted herself the thought that *now* she would be less a woman or less desirable to her husband, but remained firm in the belief that there should be no change in the conjugal relationship, and acted accordingly. As a result, her husband was barely aware of the change taking place. This is the *natural* way of the change.

Cases vary even when an enlightened regime is faithfully followed, but it is safe to say that every abnormal and undesirable symptom can be quickly overcome by rest, abstaining from certain foods, taking proper exercises and a correct outlook on life, and adopting such remedial agents as may be necessary.

Generally, the greatest enemies woman must contend with during the menopause are indigestion, dyspepsia, sluggishness of the liver, over-work, abnormal indulgence in food and drink, unhygienic surroundings, etc. If these be removed and normal habits of life established, there need be no reason for worry.

It is a universally accepted delusion that with the cessation of the periodic flow, woman naturally ceases to enjoy the embraces of her husband, and is no longer capable of conferring upon him the former satisfaction, supposedly due to the atrophying of the ovaries, and shrinking of the vaginal walls. This is a race belief which has been the cause of more misery, sorrow, broken hearts and disrupted homes, than almost all other combined influences.

This thought, always present in the mind of woman long before the time of the approaching change, has been a "thorn in flesh." Many women look forward, with dire foreboding, to the period when the *fires-of-love*—keen desire—will no longer burn within her and she will become incapable of giving the former pleasure to the man she loves, with the altogether natural expectation that he will seek satisfaction elsewhere than at his own fireside.

This constant fear and expectation unquestionably have much to do with the unnatural and undesirable change taking place, as well as with the gradual decline of the woman's desire for the usual love embrace, so that by the time the "change of life" is actually completed, her entire organism, no less than her desires and capabilities, have become paralyzed and she becomes frigid in her nature, totally at variance with her former self.

There comes to us the psychological law expressed in the

Bible as a religious truth: "The thing thou feared has come upon thee," and nowhere else in Nature is the working of the law more certain than in the domain of the emotional nature.

As a matter of absolute—and saving—truth, we can assure every woman living that there is no foundation for this destructive race belief. She may avoid becoming a victim of this inertia. She can, if she will, become many times more capable of both experiencing and giving affectional pleasure *after* the menopause, than during any other period of her life, with the possible exception of the first few times she permitted the embrace.

If a woman will keep the affectional fires burning while passing through the change of life by *willingly, and with conscious desire, accepting the conjugal embrace at least once a week between the lunar periods, being watchful that she experiences the complete climax in its highest perfection each time, she will not only keep the love nature alive and fully awakened, but she will delay the atrophying process of the ovaries and the shrinking of both uterus and the vaginal walls; becoming thereby capable of giving more intense and prolonged pleasure to her spouse than ever before, because the constant fear of pregnancy will have been entirely removed.*

Up to a comparatively *very* short time ago it was thought that only women passed through a *change of life*. Physicians, like the laity, labored under this belief. Now we *know* that men, as well as women, pass through such a *change* and at about the same age. The symptoms are very much alike in both instances:

> *Uncertainty* and a growing lack of faith in one's ability often makes its appearance. This symptom is more

pronounced in men than in women. The fear of becoming incompetent; mental depression; a seeming dullness of memory and the inability to concentrate as well as formerly, are usually more pronounced in men than in women. Other common symptoms are: Lassitude and inertia; a desire for inaction; palpitation of the heart; asthma or other ailments heretofore unknown, and fears of various kind, all without actual reason. Danger is frequently sensed, though none is present. Men easily become excited or worried without actual cause. Numbness, due to a decrease of circulation, may be felt; nerves may be taut and "on edge" much of the time. There is frequently a loss of interest in things formerly considered essential to life and happiness—a sense of failure and insecurity. Irritability and loss of control are often experienced, even in trifling, inconsequential affairs. There may be a lack of *Libido, i.e.,* the former urge for sexual relationship. In fact, this may become pronounced; more so in men than in women.

In general, Nature is giving warning that insofar as she is concerned, she is withdrawing from the scene; that the parties concerned will be obliged to follow other than former methods, and bring other forces into play if they wish to *remain* competent and fulfill the role of true *men* and *women.*

WHY SHOULD THIS BE SO? Why is it that, up to the years of forty or forty-five, the normal, healthy man is moved by a sex urge almost beyond control, and supplied with the vim and vitality to indulge inordinately, and then—almost overnight—becomes apathetic and indifferent? Why is it that the woman, who formerly had to be aroused by fondling and caressing, may now be of an entirely different nature? Why all this change?

It is as though a man had been sustained for many years to a point near heaven by some force or power, other than his own, and permitted, aye, even urged, to enjoy life to the full without personal effort; and then, suddenly, being cut off, as it were, in mid-air, with the stipulation: "If it be your desire to enjoy what has been yours for so many years, YOUR PERSONAL EFFORT MUST COMPENSATE FOR THAT WHICH WAS FREELY GIVEN YOU UP 'TILL NOW. If you fail to make this effort, and make it constantly, then all that has been yours will be lost to you."

> *Nature is utterly selfish.* She concerns herself solely and wholly with her own interests. Beginning with adolescence she sets into motion certain emotional longings and desires which automatically create forces and energies that MUST find activities and outlets in one form or another, and the most "natural" is the *biological urge*—desire for the exercise of the *libido.* This desire, almost incessant, is an incentive not so much to create as to enjoy and satisfy the urge. Nature is wise in this respect, because it assures her continued creation of the species. In man, this is a *carnal urge* which Nature instigates and keeps active so long as it serves her. In woman the desire is aroused by love's activity, or what she believes and accepts as such; induced by petting, fondling and coaxing. Man is the tempter; woman the tempted.
>
> During this period effort, on the part of man, except in the direction of self-control, is unnecessary. Whatever efforts he exerts are to hold his emotional urges in check, rather than to arouse or awaken them.

But all things must come to an end. There comes a time when Nature has obtained from man all she desires or all of which he is capable. His days of virility over, Nature arranges thus:

"Up to the present time I have given you all the power and energy required to enjoy yourself to such degree that you have been unable to resist the Urge within you. I, Nature, have been the incentive of your acts. I have been your 'devil' of pleasure. You, in turn, have been the tempter of your mate. Between you, you have served me well. You are now no longer useful to me; hence I sever my connection with you and yours. IF YOU DESIRE TO REMAIN A *man,* AND YOUR MATE A *woman,* then YOU MUST HENCEFORTH DO FOR YOURSELF THAT WHICH I HAVE PREVIOUSLY DONE FOR YOU."

NATURE IS CRUEL, BUT IN HER OWN WAY SHE IS ALSO MERCIFUL TO MAN THOUGH HE IS GENERALLY UNAWARE OF IT. ALTHOUGH SHE FORSAKES HIM AT THIS CRITICAL MOMENT, SHE DOES NOT ENTIRELY LEAVE HIM HELPLESS. HE STILL HAS THE OPPORTUNITY, AND THE ABILITY, TO DO FOR HIMSELF EVERYTHING THAT SHE HAD PREVIOUSLY DONE FOR HIM *with the exception of the capability of procreation.*

At this stage of life, what is man (this includes woman) to do? Nature gave man his virility in order that he might enjoy himself freely, and, as a result, procreate the race. God gave man something far greater than that which Nature did—HIS IMAGINATION. When the INCENTIVE of Nature is withdrawn, the IMAGINATION MUST STEP IN AND TAKE ITS PLACE.

One of the first symptoms of the oncoming "change" is the lack of the *libido* on man's part, and the loss of desire *to be* aroused on her part. THIS IS AN INERTIA WHICH IS DEATH IF PERMITTED TO CONTINUE. This

inertia is truly a prolific source of excuses: too tired;
business has been difficult; I have a headache; my back
hurts. Although there is a *feeling* of guilt, each has a
pet excuse with the result that instead of bringing the
imagination into play to arouse the desire for embrace,
they turn about and go to sleep, and weakness is added
to weakness.

It is a truism: "Constant watchfulness is the price to
be paid for continued MANHOOD AND WOMANHOOD."

Both husband and wife should have a full understanding
of the mysteries of their being, comprehending both their
strength and their weakness and work in harmony with
each other. They must become *fully conscious* of the fact
that since Nature will permit their virility to die out, it is
incumbent on their part to MAKE THE NECESSARY EFFORT
TO KEEP THEMSELVES SEXUALLY AWAKE, ACTIVE,
ALIVE. *They should agree that, if their own physical
natures will not respond automatically to a desire for the
marital embrace, they will bring the Imagination—God's
greatest gift to mankind—into activity.* This should be
done no less than once a week.

This is most readily accomplished by retrospection—by
looking into the past and recalling to mind some excep-
tionally pleasant experience of the marital pleasure which
was unforgettable. In doing this, the imaginative faculty
will do what Nature formerly did for them: SEND THE
BLOOD COURSING THROUGH THE PROCREATIVE
ORGANISM; AROUSING THE DESIRES AND BRINGING
BACK THE ABILITY TO ENJOY THE EMBRACE AS
FULLY AS BEFORE. If this method is followed from the
very beginning when Nature ceases to give help, then,

within a short period of time, a NEW CYCLE OF THE AF-
FECTIONAL NATURE IS ESTABLISHED and the *libido* on
his part, and the response on hers, will become natural and
automatic, and life will go on as before.

Question: Is it worth the effort? Is a man *man* enough to
do what is necessary to remain a *man?* Does the woman
possess enough affection to induce her to make the necessary
effort to continue a worthy object of affection? These are
questions every individual must answer for himself or herself.

If we can be successful in spreading this *law of nature* broadcast so that all men and women may come to an understanding
of its potency for the continued retention of youth, then countless homes that would otherwise be disrupted, will continue
happy and content in the knowledge that all is well.

Let every man and woman look forward to a greater fulfill-
ment of life *after* the menopause, giving extra care and attention
to the entire system while passing through the change, keeping
alive the entire being—mind, body and Soul—by recreation;
the mental faculties awake and active, the body virile through
exercise. Let them attend good plays, associate with refined,
cheerful people; enjoy life; never mention the change that is
taking place, except to the physician; consistently refuse to
recognize a morbid side of life. Let them eat only those foods
which will continue to rebuild the mental and nervous system;
creating the vital forces to maintain balance and equilibrium.

Just as the girl entering womanhood should be prohibited
from intensive and hard work, so should the woman entering
menopause avoid the strenuous activities she previously enjoyed.
The system may require an extra supply of nerve energy beginning with the menopause, and, to be at her best, possibly
throughout the remainder of her life. Frequently, at this period

of her life, a woman is like a ship at sea, carrying a heavy load during a storm. If she is to hold her course and safely reach port, speed must be reduced, so that there may be a reserve of power for all emergencies.

Once the change has been completed, she may no longer require the extra strength and vitality previously necessary for her well-being; nor will she need to recover the loss sustained every month by the lunar flow; thus will she be stronger, capable of greater effort, and possess the power of showing deeper affection for her husband.

A serious error of the past, and one still prevalent, is the generally accepted opinion that menopause is a disease; an evil from which there is no escape. Undoubtedly, there has been good reason for such a conclusion, because those who previously enjoyed health, strength and marital pleasures no sooner enter upon the *change in life*—for such it is—than they become afflicted with various ailments and weaknesses, all more or less serious in themselves, and becoming more serious if neglected.

Menopause is an entirely natural functional change from *creative usefulness* to *creative rest.* Instead of heralding disease, misery and, not infrequently, life-long suffering, it should be, and *can be,* the herald of health and strength; a time for the enjoyment of the fruits of the past period of life.

During the change of life, any latent weakness that had not actively manifested previously may exhibit itself and at a time when the system is unprepared for the extra strain. Instead of displaying wisdom and seeking the actual cause, usually to be found in lack of exercise, indulgence in congesting foods, overwork, unsanitary conditions, unwholesome surroundings and sexual abuses, the menopause is blamed for it. Actually, menopause has nothing whatever to do with such weakness or suffering other than possibly furnishing an avenue for their manifestation.

The change of life should never be an occasion for fear and dread, but should rather be welcomed as an opportunity for greater peace and contentment; a deeper mental, physical, spiritual satisfaction. If harmony has been established in the system, menopause will proceed normally and the body will enjoy freedom from many of its former weaknesses.

One fact cannot be too strongly impressed upon the mind of every woman, namely: if afflicted with what is usually termed "female weakness," she will suffer more or less during the change *unless corrective measures are taken,* and should hardly expect the change itself to be a cure-all, or the means of freeing her from such ailments. In fact, the change of life may even intensify the condition; establish chronic invalidism, hysterical, nervous or irrational moments with the result that life will be made miserable for her and all members of the family.

Recommendation: Immediately after it becomes apparent that the "change" is beginning or has commenced, a reliable physician should be consulted; blood count checked; blood-pressure taken; cardiograph and a urinalysis made.

Any abnormality should be corrected by proper treatment. In many instances, the services of an experienced Endocrinologist will be of great aid in helping women to pass through the change naturally and normally and with the least inconvenience. Glandular (biological) substances long since have proved their efficacy. These recommendations, be it remembered, are as important to men as they are to women.

CONTINENCE IN THE UNMARRIED

T HE continent life, as related to the unmarried, is apparently an extremely simple proposition; but after a moment of serious thought, it assumes appalling proportions, more especially when we give thought to the various complications in relation to the different temperaments and ages from youth to dotage.

The continent life is endorsed for the single, whether man or woman; irrespective of age, color, creed or clime even after the most careful consideration and long experience of both its desirability and possible ill effects.

Many writers on this subject, both of the past and present, writers who are recognized internationally as authorities and whose conclusions have been accepted unquestionably, have based their deductions on the laws governing animal life and action. It is extremely doubtful if any of these writers ever lived outside of the city limits or had any extensive experience with animal life.

It is almost certain that had these writers fortified their knowledge by a more or less prolonged stay in the country where animal life abounds, surrounded by cows, horses, goats and other animals, they would have been more wary in basing their conclusions on animal habits and practices.

Because those of us who have lived in rural districts for many years and have gone directly to Nature for first-hand information, *have witnessed, time and again, hence know as a fact,* that the stallion, the bull, the goat and other animals, constantly practice masturbation after reaching a certain age;

that this practice may become so pronounced and do such
great harm to the animal, that it has become necessary for
breeders of valuable stock to use saltpetre to reduce the urge
of the animal and to arrange their stalls to make the practice
next to impossible

This is an ugly truth, but one which generally understood,
will compel many accepted authorities to seek in other than
the animal for knowledge upon which to base their theories
dealing with sex practices.

Practically all teachers of the subject who did not base
their conclusions on what they believe to be the laws and habits
governing the animal kingdom, relied rather on their misunderstanding of Nature's laws, telling us that it is *natural* for
man to live the continent life while remaining single.

This inference is as erroneous as the first, because the law
governing throughout all the realms of creative nature is:
*As soon as sentient creatures reach the age where reproduction
is possible they mate, cohabit regularly in the season, being governed exclusively by their instincts; and many, in fact, most
animals, are decidedly polygamic.*

Nature does not question whether reproduction really results.
It is an actual fact that in numerous instances, especially
with finely bred animals, it is necessary to mate them time
after time before conception occurs.

Thus, throughout the domain of nature, instinct and season
alone is recognized. There is absolutely no governing code
of morality or honor, and the only law obeyed is: *Use the
function and forces of reproduction just as soon as they are
sufficiently developed, and continue their exercise, whenever
possible, until age ends all.*

This is the *fiat* of Nature and decidedly no more desirable for humanity to obey than are the instincts governing animals and inciting them to action. A comprehension and acceptance of these facts will urge us to seek more deeply for a rule of action which is applicable to mankind and in harmony with God's great purpose.

What then is this Law?

Simply this: Man is dual in his nature. First, the animal or creative instinct, the biological *urge,* governs his desires and he generally obeys them. In fact, few ever gain the knowledge and strength to wisely control the function. Possibly this is well, otherwise creation might cease.

Second, the Divine inheritance; a consciousness giving man the right of choice. Knowing and feeling the urge of his human and animal nature, he possesses a mind with which he can keep in check the desires of his lower nature.

Concisely stated, this implies that at the dictation of his Divine nature, he exercises the creative, or animal function only when his higher self indicates that it is best for him to do so.

We say "best" advisedly, because the code of morality changes from age to age. What is believed right in this day may be considered totally wrong in the near future. This is clearly indicated in the Biblical stories recording acts which today would be pronounced as criminal, but at the time of their consummation were blessed of God, because *necessary* to the continuation of the race.

Neither the instinct which governs the action of animals, nor the laws of Nature, as generally understood, are applicable to the action of *enlightened* man. We base our conclusions

and instructions on the indisputable fact that man is an
accountable being, possessing the privilege of *free choice.*
Within him are two entirely separate personalities, one governed by Natural Law and *carnal* desire; the other by the
Divine Prompting of God; *maintaining throughout that this
Higher Law should govern his creative acts;* permitting exercise of the function only when to the best interest of humanity,
himself, and God's great purpose.

Almost from the moment of birth there is an urge in the
creature, whether animal or human, to exercise the creative
function. As days pass into weeks, weeks into months, months
into years, this incitant, with the awakening desire, continues
to increase in intensity until the time of adolescence, when
the craving for indulgence is well nigh uncontrollable.

This is comprehensible when we are aware that only because
of this constant urge is the world populated. Were it not
for this uncontrolled longing, the knowledge of pain following the birth of a new creature, and the grave responsibility
involved, would induce practically all in the feminine world
to refuse the union which results in a new creation. The constant urge and desire to exercise the creative function, is, as
we have said, Nature's law for her own protection—a law
that still governs the majority of mankind.

No effort is required on the part of anyone, except physical
weaklings, to have this inherent craving for sexual indulgence
increase with the bodily growth. It is Mother Nature herself
acting within the bosom of the creature, so that it shall
become a co-creator with her.

All this is indisputable and is readily proven by the well
known fact that we find among children of the most tender
years, both male and female, those who practice abuse and

continue it until either weakness or death, knowledge of un-desirable results, or marital relationship takes its place.

The child is a product of Nature and develops harmoniously with her laws, which means that it inherits the strength and the vices of the animal kingdom, with all its tendencies; there is no need to instruct it in practices which belong to both the animal and natural realms, *this being an inherent cell-consciousness.*

As previously mentioned, within the animal body, the car-nal man, with its animal instincts there is an inherent potency not possessed by the rest of the animal creation; *this we term the Divine Principle;* the Bible calls it the *"seed."* [1] Generally this is dormant in all children, and may remain so during all of life, the natural and animal natures being allowed to govern every action.

Here we have the *key* to the entire problem. It indicates a method for the instruction of the youth, through obedience to which he will be enabled to live the continent life and set aside, for the time being, both natural and animal laws, and thus reap a great benefit, rather than a weakness.

This desirable result is possible only through a systematic course of instruction and training of the youth, thereby arous-ing the Divine nature in man, having it keep pace with the development of the creative animal nature, meanwhile con-trolling it. This is not as difficult as one might suppose, though it unquestionably requires self-control and denial.

The method necessitates the thorough instruction of every youth in creative laws, moral codes, and his own Divine

---

[1] This *Divine Principle,* or *seed* spoken of so many times in the Bible is not the seed of pro-creation, but the *spirit* of that seed and its purpose is REgenera-tion. In considering *Race Regeneration* this must be constantly kept in mind.

possibilities; the inculcation of a thorough understanding of the purpose of the creative organism and the correct exercise of the function for *three specific purposes,* namely: reproduction; RE-creation, or the reconstruction of the self being, and RE-*generation.*

Merely teaching the youths these laws would not be any more desirable than locking the safety valve in a steam engine to prevent the escape of steam when the pressure became greater than the power of resistance of the boiler. If understanding *and protection* is sought, there must be a thorough knowledge of the power and use of the forces, *as well as a natural and divinely accepted method for the use, reabsorption, or transmutation of the superfluous energy.*

We are aware that the man or woman who is given to extremely hard physical labor, to worry, anxiety, intense study, or exercise and training requiring great nerve and muscular force, is, for the time being, practically free from the *libido* or *urge* of the procreative nature. This clearly indicates a method whereby the functions may be controlled without detrimental effects on the being.

First: A careful selection of food, including in the dietary only those articles which contain the maximum amount of nerve, brain and rebuilding material, and the minimum of stimulating, irritating and congesting substances; a wise selection of drinks, avoiding those stimulating and exciting, such as tea and coffee; all alcoholic beverages and so-called "soft" drinks, these latter actually causing an irritation of the kidneys, having a direct exciting action on the sexual organism, often more destructive than beer or light wine, and in many respects equally as harmful as other alcoholic drinks.

Second: Frequent bathing to cleanse the system of all congestions; keeping the pores of the skin free from poisonous substances, and helping it to perform its functions by absorbing plenty of fresh air.

Third: Careful selection of wearing apparel, choosing the clothing for comfort as well as appearance; not too tight; porous, thus allowing fresh air to reach the skin. Wearing woolen clothing next to the skin is highly undesirable except in the aged—those who have reached senility. The universal practice of having children and youths wear woolen underwear cannot be too severely condemned.

Fourth: Exercise is of vast importance. Proper exercise not only develops the body, nerves, and muscles, exhilarating the mind; it also forces the circulation to "draw up" much of the vital fluids which promote growth; giving incentive to the mind and strengthening the character; thereby greatly lessening or neutralizing the desire for sexual gratification.

Fifth: Association. Possibly nothing else with the exception of food, has such a vast influence on the desires as have associates. Whenever possible, these should be selected from youths of like ages, known to be of clean habits and chaste language; also of people much older, capable of instilling moral courage, worthy incentives and a longing for achievement. The cleanest mind and purest heart can quickly be poisoned by continually listening to suggestive word picturing.

Sixth: Recreation. This is essential to the well-being of every boy and girl and should include games, dramas, motion pictures and dancing. All games requiring muscular activity and nerve tensioning will help to naturally use up the stored creative energy and, at the same time, elevate the mind, lifting the thoughts from the physical to the mental and spiritual.

All dances, plays, operas and games suggestive or sex-arousing in their tendency should be prohibited.

Seventh: Sleep is likewise important; the hours to be carefully regulated, arranging the time for retiring so that it is possible to at once fall asleep; arising immediately after awakening in the morning; followed by a cool bath and physical exercises.

Eighth: Teaching *personal responsibility.* The child and youth should consistently be taught *personal responsibility for every act.* They should be impressed with the fact that a vicarious atonement cannot relieve them of the penalty resulting from a non-good act; nor withhold the reward for well-doing. They must be instructed in the function of the creative organism and made to realize that the exercise for mere pleasure produces a loss which cannot be replaced and paves the way for weakness and disease; depletion of creative energy of body, nerves and mind; *directly affecting the Soul itself. This, relative to religious practices, exerts a powerful influence on the Spiritual part of man.*

Ninth: The inculcation of the law that every act and thought having effect on the sexual organism has a direct influence on the mind, the nerves, and also on the Soul, and its future welfare *here and hereafter.* Every drain upon the creative organism is potent for evil on the mind and Soul and lessens the possibility of Immortality; sexual exercise being allowable only *by the action of the Will,* for *procreation;* for the *recreation* of the self; and the RE-*generation* of the Spiritual in man; pleasure being an essential part of the act, but of secondary nature.

Tenth: A complete system of breathing exercises which

enables one to draw the seminal fluids *by the action of the Will,* directly into the circulation, helping in the storing of vital force, mental and nerve power, and toward Spiritualization. This is a direct RE-*generative* process which enables those who practice it, to avoid the body, mind and Soul shattering cravings which often overcome the strongest men and women who do not possess this knowledge of the transmutation of the forces.

Thus far we have given our consideration only to the youth. Admittedly it is much easier to deal with these than with that other large class composed of men and women who have reached the age of full maturity and responsibility, but who, for reasons of their own, remain unmarried.

With the youth we can begin the correct training at an early age, but with the other class greater difficulties are to be overcome because many of them have always had the wrong perspective of life and action; have been taught and trained incorrectly, and possibly have long since become the victims of degrading habits. Generally, the identical methods must be followed by all, irrespective of the age of the individual.

Natural Laws intend that men and women, having passed the period of adolescence, should mate and become the head of a family. The early development of the procreative functions indicate this clearly. Custom and the grave responsibilities involved have, unfortunately, made this impractical in all too many instances. Many regrettable errors and degrading vices could undoubtedly be avoided if youths were in position to marry shortly after attaining manhood and womanhood.

We are constantly brought into touch with men whose mothers have led them to believe that the modern woman is not desirable as a wife, or to become the mother of children; that they no longer possess the virtues of true womanliness. On this basis they urge their sons to remain single. In all too many instances these mothers actually believe what they preach, but in the majority of cases, their argument is based on selfishness or a complex. Unfortunately, also, many widely accepted "authorities" would have men believe that there are no longer any virtuous women.

In proportion to the number of women, possibly not as large a percentage of them would make as good wives and mothers as formerly; nevertheless, there is no dearth of women who, because of their greater knowledge, would actually make *better* wives, mothers, sweethearts and companions than heretofore. Life in itself is more or less an experiment. No mother is ever justified in preventing a son or daughter from marrying. No man or woman should allow fear or cowardice to prevent him or her from seeking a mate because of the possibility of making a mistake.

Life is, as said, an experiment; a glorious or a dreadful one, depending altogether on how we look at it or the kind of material of which we are made. God allowed man—or his Soul—to embody in the flesh and come to the earth plane that he might gain knowledge THROUGH EXPERIENCE; or, as He Himself said: "That man might come to know good and evil." Why then evade the opportunity? Greater wisdom is gained by making mistakes, THEN IN CORRECTING THEM.

All too frequently both men and women fear to enter the marital state because harmony, hence happiness, was entirely lacking in their homes. Actually, because of their knowledge of these experiences, they have the greatest possibility for happiness. They have learned in advance the things which bring about inharmony and failure in marriage and, possessing this knowledge, can avoid similar experiences.

Only the coward avoids responsibilities. God's great Law *is*—Mate; properly and wisely. Man's first effort should be to gain the knowledge of what actually constitutes being a *Man;* the responsibilities of a lover, husband and father, then wisely seek a mate and do his best. This is man's sacred duty.

Frequently we are called upon to deal with men and women who, disappointed in a first affair of the heart, are actually dead in their emotional nature. There are others who avoid marriage because they labor under the fear of an inherent transmittable or incurable disease.

These, like the youth, should live the continent, REgenerative life. If work, exercise, recreation, the transmutation of the vital forces and strict obedience to the Divine Law are adhered to, health, strength, peace of mind and final happiness will be theirs.

The Law of Life is based on mating and the reproduction of the species. Marriage is the medium for the proper utilization of the creative forces and energies, first in reproduction, then for health, strength and well-being.

The exchange of these forces between the twain bring about these desirable conditions, and finally, the REgeneration of their being; "mortality putting on Immortality," as commanded by the Divine Law. Marriage begins in the passion of youth and generation, but should end in affection and companionship during advanced age — with the possibility of Immortalization for both. This in truth, is the *way* to the REGENERATION OF THE RACE.

THE PATH OF DEATH *

"The Soul That Sinneth, It Shall Die"

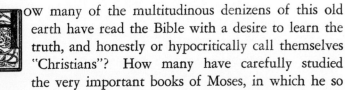ow many of the multitudinous denizens of this old earth have read the Bible with a desire to learn the truth, and honestly or hypocritically call themselves "Christians"? How many have carefully studied the very important books of Moses, in which he so emphatically commands man to *avoid* "casting his seed upon the ground"? How many of those who have read the Sacred Scriptures — so-called because they teach the law — have actually obeyed these Laws in act and spirit?

It is safe to say that this Divine *fiat* has been more or less impressed upon the men who have been sincere in their search and study. However, only a comparatively few really comprehend that in this edict is contained the *law* of life and death to man as an individual, and to the race in general.

Disobedience to this one command in the "garden" (the beginning of conscious man) has been the cause of wars and rumors of war, sin and sickness, misery and finally death; in short, it started all of the undesirable conditions which have in the past, and which still enslave, mankind. Except for man's first disobedience to this Divine command—which is the Law of Life or death—depending on whether it is obeyed

*The act or acts discussed in this Chapter constitutes what is in reality the *path of death*. We humbly suggest that those who question this fact obtain a good Bible Concordance and carefully look up all the references dealing with the "seed." It is certain that a grim awakening awaits them.

or ignored—life on earth would be a heavenly, blissful experience instead of the proverbial "daily grind."

"The Soul that sinneth, it shall die."—*Ezek.* 18: 4, 20, is an eternal, irrevocable law, and is directly applicable to man's almost universal practice of giving his *"seed* unto Moloch"; —*Lev.* 20: 2, *i.e.,* the "casting of the seed upon the ground" in one manner or another because this is the wasting, *i.e.,* unholy destruction, of the universal, *creative* substance out of which man is created and is the supply material for the "temples not made with hands" which alone can "house" Souls. It is the universal substance, God-given to man for both procreation or generation and for his spiritual RE-generation.

In the ultimate it is immaterial by what specific act or acts man casts his seed upon the ground; whether he be married and living a form of prostitution with his legalized wife, committing some form of pollution, masturbation, *Coitus Interruptus* or any other Biblically condemned practice.

The ultimate *result* will almost invariably be the same, with but slight variations, except that possibly one type of behavior is more "beastly" than the other—with apologies to the beasts of the field.

Sodomism and other perversions are admittedly more degrading, even in thought and desire, than the unsanctioned, *i.e.,* UNSANCTIFIED, acts engaged in by men and women during the marital rite.

Of all the unnatural practices in married life, pollution as the result of non-completion of the rite, or, as in Biblical language, "casting the seed upon the ground,"—to Moloch— is probably the most disgusting and Soul degrading, while the immediately harmful effect is in *Coitus Interruptus.*

Consulting any modern medical text on the subject—and many are published especially for the laity—it quickly becomes apparent that *Coitus* is possible only as a result of the blood rushing into the male organ of generation. The male in turn brings about the same result in the female by coddling, endearments, etc.

In normal, natural *Coitus* the desire of both, and movements in harmony with the desire, will bring about a climax or sensation, resulting in immediate release, followed by the relaxation of the entire system, ESPECIALLY the nervous system, with a normalization of the blood circulation.

If the marital embrace is all it should be, mentally, physically and spiritually, then there will follow a feeling of general well-being; a let-down as it were, with a desire for rest.

However, if the Rite is engaged in, both parties brought to a high state of excitement until it would almost seem that the organism could bear no more, and then the act is left unfinished *(Coitus Interruptus),* the parties separating, there will be no immediate let-down, no relaxation of the nervous system, but, on the contrary, an intensification of excitement and the blood will not at once recede; leaving the organism calm and satisfied.

> If this practice is repeated time and again, it will result in ovarian congestion and inflammation, causing various diseases of the woman's generative system, shattered nerves on her part, and Prostatitis on his part, ending finally in some form of surgical operation for both. Uncountable such operations each year are traceable directly to this vicious practice.
>
> That is not all. Perhaps long before there is need of such operations, there is disgust on her part, and hatred on

his part, because he will despise himself for the practice, but blame her for his difficulties. It is reasonable to estimate that eighty-five per cent of all operations for Prostatitis, eighty per cent of what are generally classed as "female diseases," are made necessary because of the practice of *Coitus Interruptus* in some form or another. In addition to the damage to the physical well-being, fully eighty per cent of the sorrow, misery, hatred and disgust in conjugal relations is traceable to these practices, hence the "hells" in life and the consequent breaking up of homes.

It is the universal disobedience to the commands voiced by Moses and other Biblical writers against throwing *"any* of the 'seed' to Moloch" that is directly responsible for many of the miseries in the world. Men and women continually prostitute themselves, draining the life forces to the very dregs, casting them aside as so much rubbish, that a carnal passion may be satisfied. For a moment's pleasure a terrific price is paid in moral weakness, physical suffering and mental degradation.

Contrary to all that has been taught by those who fail to comprehend clearly the subject, we maintain that the sex desire is not abnormal, not an inheritance which came to man gradually as he fell from his high estate. "Male and female created He them,"—hence the creative organism of the male as of the female were made a part of them.

God did not create these organs for the mere satisfaction of having accomplished the theretofore unknown, but because He *intended them for a noble purpose—a specific purpose—procreation and recreation.*

It is unreasonable and illogical to believe that desire was

not given man and woman at that same moment of creation; because *where desire is unknown, use is not made of a potency or principle.*

We therefore condemn and exclude those unreasonable teachings which would have us believe that the creative desire did not come to man until after he had *fallen* from his high estate.

Such instructions induce people to believe that sex longings are unnatural and unholy, causing them to attempt suppression, and by stifling a natural impulse they create an abnormal condition, generally ending in degrading vices and indulgence in Soul-searing rites and debaucheries.

We firmly contend there is nothing impure in the entire department of sex, nor unnatural in the normal desire; although we freely admit that there are all too many unsanctioned exercises of the creative function, which end in sorrow, misery and ultimately in death. It is the perversion to which the function is subjected that is objectionable, destructive and degrading. One must be reasonable and differentiate right use and its desirable results from abuse or non-use and the penalty which sin visits upon the transgressor.

We emphatically condemn the inimical teachings that creative desire is destructive to the spiritual nature in man. As a fact, the contrary is true; although it must be understood that the appetite should be normal and indulgence not merely for pleasure. The selfish passion must be held in strict abeyance, while the purpose of the Rite should be either generation or RE-generation. There is no sin in the ecstacy that accompanies a "deed well done."

Because of the pernicious teachings, leading the mass to believe that normal sex desire is destructive to the spiritual nature in man, many follow the Path of Death. On the one hand we have those who attempt to kill out all desire, thereby destroying the *source* of power in man—the foundation of his spiritual REgeneration and redemption; while on the other hand are the advocates of license and unbridled passion, giving free rein to their passion in promiscuous relationship and free love—damning the Soul and making moral lepers of themselves.

The strength of the creative energy is to the human being what steam is to the engine. The greater the amount of steam the more power; provided always that it is directed along the proper channels and held under control. Similarly, the stronger the creative power in man, when combined with normal desire, the greater are his possibilities for achievement; provided, also that these energies are directed along the right channels—for generation and REgeneration.

That sex desires, the *Libido,* are normal throughout *all* Nature, is clearly indicated by the animal, which though not mating at all times, does seek the satisfaction of Nature's fulfillment when in season. This cannot be termed the carnal nature, but rather the creative nature within the animal, which at certain seasons, awakens in order to perpetuate its species.

Many writers and educators do not seem to grasp the difference between man and animal, failing to take into consideration several important factors. The animal seeks mating only *during* the Lunar season, while the human seeks satisfaction between the Lunar periods. The animal nature is a *single* one; is entirely carnal or animal, while man's nature is *triplicate:* (1) Animal or carnal; (2) Love and/or affectional; (3) Spiritual or REgenerative. If man is *enlightened,* truly *man,* then all of his three natures coordinate in *unison* during the marital rite.

That which creative urge has been unable to accomplish in the animal is achieved in the human—the diabolical reasoning which induces the male to leave the female when masculine passion is satisfied, or at the request of the female. It is *not* because of his creative desires that man has, in all too many instances, become degraded to a degree lower than the beast, but through the abominable and degrading practices by which he attempts to sate his appetites.

Truth is all too frequently unpleasant to hear, and this is particularly true when sex is the problem under consideration. However, if we are men and women, and not merely males and females—weaklings and degenerates—we will be keenly willing to use our reasoning faculties and give careful consideration to this most important subject from every perspective.

The normal enlightened, healthy man, selects a time for all things, and although he may be one of the most virile of men, he would not think of attempting to satisfy his desire except at the proper time.

When a man does otherwise, it is clearly an indication of either ignorance or weakness, or of some diseased condition lurking within. Generally, we partake of three meals a day. This becomes a habit and we have a sense of hunger at certain times each day without mentally dwelling on the subject. We pursue our business, vocation, or profession with neither thought nor desire for food except at the proper time.

In like manner the healthy man gives his attention to the duties before him and refuses to permit his mind to dwell on carnal satisfaction. When the "time is propitious" he seeks his mate and they embrace naturally and in holiness. This is Nature's and God's plan.

It is sad indeed, to contemplate the many who live to eat and drink, rather than eat and drink to live, and who make free use of drugs to free the body of congestions resulting from over-indulgence, in order that they may indulge again.

These are on a par with the man who exercises his creative ability, stopping short of the actual *climax,* that he may shortly indulge again and enjoy his carnal pleasure; wholly ignorant of the fact that he is setting up an inflammation which will shortly make it impossible to have a normal marital embrace, and that his "sin" is as great and as destructive as that of the man guilty of "casting his seed upon the ground."

For the true man, love must be the actuating force; the true, normal and healthy male never, for a moment, considers it wise or desirable to have congress with a woman for whom he has neither affection nor love.

With primitive man there was but one consideration; the object in view was procreation; he had not as yet attained to the knowledge of the human Soul, or the possibility of its Im-mortalization by means of REgeneration.

There may have been love in his breast for his mate and a desire for children, but beyond this his reasoning faculties did not go. It is even possible, that as in the animal kingdom of today, his mate had only a certain period during which she sought the embrace and the male, knowing no other law, was obedient to her wish.

We no longer belong to the primitive ancestors, although in some respects we are less civilized, if civilization is based on morality and spirituality.

We have the power of reasoning; the comprehension and understanding that there is in man more than can be satisfied by eating, drinking, sleeping, and a pleasurable act through which procreation is made possible. We feel within ourselves that we are dual; that while we have a desire to live and enjoy, and to give pleasure, we are constantly seeking the ideal and longing for an understanding of the laws leading to spiritual consciousness. Of all this the primitive man was wholly ignorant; therefore it is illogical to analyze the creative impulses from his standpoint.

Unquestionably, there was much in the primitive man that moderns could well accept as examples after which to pattern their own lives. The primitive man was well satisfied with the association of one woman, and because of this, his creative organism did not become inflamed as so often happens at the present time when men indulge promiscuously, absorbing the mixed magnetic forces of numerous women.

This is always destructive to both health and stability of mind. When, to satisfy the passions, men or women indulge in *Coitus* with different persons within a limited time, the blood becomes a mixture of different forces.

This creates a *consuming* fire in the blood, a constantly increasing desire for more frequent indulgence, creating an irritation or inflammation of the creative organism, which, like *Coitus Interruptus,* ends in prostatitis in him, ovarian inflammation or congestion or other serious ailments in her; and in both, a nervous instability.

Furthermore, our primitive ancestors *lived* as far as we can gather, in harmony with the greatest of all laws; the one so consistently inculcated by Moses, through which he attempted to save his people from the fearful diseases which were ravaging them. These diseases had their inception in continuous indulgence to the point of satisfaction, and then discontinuing for the moment; thereby cheating themselves, and their female victims; defying God's greatest law; damning themselves and those guilty with them.

The great mass of men have not yet become acquainted with the absolute law, that man has not the slightest right, even though married, to embrace the woman unless he is actuated by love. To seek the embrace when passion and desire, minus love, is the incentive, is to commit an unholy act. It is prostitution, resulting in mutual hate, sex degeneration, ending in impotency; and if a child results, it may be a weakling, an idiot, or with tendencies toward crime or insanity.

The sex function with all its potentialities, when used solely for creation and (self) REcreation, is the highest gift of God to man. It makes of man a co-creator with God. By the *uplifting* of this force, "mortality is enabled to put on Immortality." It is the one potent factor for continued youth, health, beauty and longevity.

On the contrary, the abuse of the function is the cause, now as it always has been, of all the plagues that have appalled humanity throughout the ages. If one is seeking a picturization of the grave results of these abuses, he needs but read understandingly the Biblical narrative of Moses with his children in the wilderness.

The race was threatened with extinction by abuses and degenerative practices. It was saved only by his timely intervention and the discontinuation of self-pollution on the one hand, and the discontinuation of "casting of the seed upon the ground" on the other.

Their salvation was symbolized by the "raising of the serpent," *i.e.,* the LIFTING UP, or SPIRITUALIZATION, of all that belongs to sex.

Correct use of any potency, assuming that this includes normal use, is the *only* method to greater power. The *abuse* of any potential inheritance produces a gradual weakening and ultimate destruction, the dissipation of that power. Especially is this true regarding all pertaining to sex.

We repeat with emphasis another law governing man in his relationship with woman and entirely separate from those already mentioned, but which is of equal importance, if he aspires to reach his highest development. While it is indisputable that the *greatest* consideration that should govern the embrace is *love,* it is equally true that he must approach her only by gaining her consent, preparing her through caresses and the endearments so highly prized by every true and normal woman.

No man has any right to *possess* a woman until he has first aroused her to an active desire to be possessed. Many a woman considered as frigid, or actually almost dormant in feeling, may be aroused to the heights of the love passion by well directed caresses. The basis of all sex relationship *must* be mutual consent sanctioned by love.

We condemn, with all our might, the practice of countless men, termed husbands, taking forcible possession of their wedded partners, considering them bound to comply because of a marriage certificate. This constitutes rape in the spiritual sense, as certainly as it is rape when a man forces a woman not his wife—especially one of immature age—into compliance.

White slavery so universally condemned is not one whit worse and no greater cause of sorrow than is the prostitution continually practiced between countless men and women, who, though married, have no love for each other, and who, in many instances, actually hate and despise each other.

A white slave is one who, contrary to her desires, is made a prisoner and is forced to receive attentions which are repulsive to her, until finally she is willing to lead an immoral life without compulsion.

Where is there any actual difference between the woman of "ill fame" who sells her body, and the husbanded lady, who, for one reason or another, permits favors revolting to her nature, while possibly hating or bearing malice toward her husband? Not alone does the woman suffer, but he, also, is severely punished; the incentive may be different; the ultimate results are identical.

We have frequently said that women, especially those married, have become slaves to the passions of their husbands. What of the numberless instances where husbands truly love their wives, obeying the laws in their entirety, never approaching them except with caresses and consent, but who, time and again, are allowed the privilege only upon a promise to be "careful"?

Plainly stated, she consents only after he agrees to "cast his seed upon the ground," thereby *protecting* her, but committing the crime which Moses forbade all people under penalty of death to the Soul.

Foolish man! Because he loves and desires, he complies with her request, only to find that for some unknown reason, she becomes less lovable and more irritable; harder to please, more unsatisfied and fault-finding; while he comes to care less for her and finds himself gradually losing his strength and virility, thoroughly disgusted with all that concerns sex and womankind.

THE PATH OF DEATH

PERVERSIONS

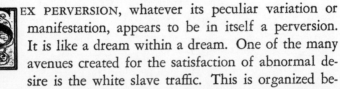EX PERVERSION, whatever its peculiar variation or manifestation, appears to be in itself a perversion. It is like a dream within a dream. One of the many avenues created for the satisfaction of abnormal desire is the white slave traffic. This is organized because of the demand for women to be exploited for generally accepted immoral purposes. Young and innocent girls are often desired by men rich in worldly goods. These have usually become so thoroughly satiated with the more common abuses of the creative function that they continually seek for satisfaction in ways out of the ordinary, and they possess the means to have this want supplied.

This is only one of the many reasons for the exploitation of God's greatest gift to humanity. It usually leads to degradation first and spiritual destruction in the end. It would probably take a large volume to separate and classify all of the reasons. Among the specific reasons are some not at all due to degeneracy, but to the biological urge on the one side, and ignorance on the other.

First among these are the countless single men of all ages who are well sexed with a strong *Libido,* who have never had instructions for its control, or how they might make constructive, and even *Immortalizing* or REgenerative use of the creative forces by wisely and correctly directing them.

These have no thought of committing DEgenerative acts.

Their sole search is for physical—nerve and mental relief—and this is the only means known to them.

Another large number of those patronizing houses of ill repute are as innocent in intent as the class just named. These are found among that almost uncountable number of men who are married and who should find satisfaction at home, but whose wives are naturally frigid. That the wives of such men, or many of them, are utterly selfish, self-satisfied, or perhaps were victims of the husband's ignorance at the beginning of married life, is beside the point. The fact remains that they have sealed up both affection and desire within themselves and refuse to comply with their husband's wishes, except occasionally under what amounts to compulsion. In such instances both husbands and wives are in a manner innocent of evil intent, but their unnatural way of living invariably ends in the brothel or solitary vice; in degradation; dissatisfaction, or possibly grave diseases, both mental and physical.

If a count could be taken, it would probably be found that these two classes mentioned—without intent of any specific wrong—outnumber all others in their support of houses of ill-repute, except during periods of war.

How to remedy this destructive, demoralizing and degenerating condition is the great problem confronting mankind. This problem must be solved and the remedy applied if the nations are to be redeemed from the disintegration that is slowly, but surely, taking place. Sex perversions indulged in by an ever increasing percentage of the people must lead to the eventual crumbling of the very foundation of human society.

History, in all too many instances, has informed us that when sex degeneracy becomes universal, it dooms that nation whose people are most guilty. It is like a malignant cancer eating away the very heart of the people. In the past it has been the main cause of the downfall of great nations. Virility of man alone makes great nations possible, and virility and manhood are surely destroyed by perversive practices.

In seeking for the cause of debasing practices and the resulting degeneracy, are we willing to accept the revealing truth when we are confronted with it?

If we are, we will soon learn that, generally, the parents whose sons and daughters follow the left-handed path have themselves been deeply guilty, though all too often ignorantly so, of constantly and consistently infringing upon creative laws. Possibly the child was undesired, hence cursed in thought and feeling throughout the days of the mother's pregnancy. Possibly the mother was frigid or unaroused by affection and the marital rite was repugnant to her when conception took place. There are in truth and fact hundreds of "perhapses" involved.

Admittedly, it is not always the fault of one or both of the parents that the child becomes a pervert, *but there is always a cause.* Exceptions only prove the rule and even in the isolated cases it will be found that, like in the inheritance of syphilis or other inheritable diseases, the tendency may be handed down from grandparents or great grandparents.

The one and only remedy that will dispel the ignorance pervading humanity relative to the creative function and everything that is associated with it, consists in the constant explanation of the PURPOSE of sex, the SACREDNESS OF SEX, and the observance of the creative laws as laid down by Sacred literature, *i.e., as a religious duty essential to the salvation of man's Soul.*

There must be a most emphatic preachment of the many
fearful penalties that *must* be paid by *every* one who ignores or infringes upon the Law. In this manner alone
can there be any hope for the regeneration of the race—
for the restoration of mankind to primitive purity and the
establishment of a higher civilization.

One of the greatest and most direct causes of the wide-
spread and colossal ignorance of the races of men concerning the physical, moral and sacred aspects of sex, its right
use and the penalty for abuse, must be laid at the door of
the established churches.

Religious leaders have not dared to bring this problem
into the open so that the cleansing and curative light of
knowledge might shine upon it. Instead, they have
ignored every reference to the awful penalties of sex
abuses, for "casting the seed upon the ground."

They have also left unsaid what might have been taught
concerning the blessings of the creative act as one of the
fundamentals for the immortalization of the Soul.

Of the virtuous who fall victims to the wiles of panderers
and degenerates, let us take for example the girl who is drawn
into the meshes of a white slave organization. Admitting that
she does suffer the tortures of mind and Soul so often depicted,
is it true that she is entirely blameless?

Some girls are enticed away from home and friends, while
others, more beautiful and seemingly more desirable, remain
unmolested.

Why is this true?

Possibly if we were to seek deeply for the cause we would
find in this "going astray" a desire for adventure; that pleasure,
jewels and beautiful clothes held greater attraction for them

than the love of home and family and pride in innocence, and that this was the lure employed by exploiters in inducing them to forsake all that is real in life for an apparently glittering future.

Instinctively, these girls, though of good heart, are dissatisfied with their home life, friends, and the ordinary pleasures the community affords. They look with longing eyes to those other possessions and pleasures of which so much has been written. What is the result?

When the flashy, versatile stranger appears, he is quick to note the dissatisfaction and seeks acquaintance; he plays upon the emotions as does the master musician on the harp; he fires the imagination, and holds out glittering promises of all and everything in heaven and earth. Admittedly, nearly every one of these girls is honest at heart, but all scruples are readily overcome by the false promise of ease of life, or even honorable marriage.

We have indicated several reasons why it is apparently easy for the exploiters of virtue to find victims; because of the dissatisfaction of these girls with their environments, friends, possessions and pleasures. There is an inborn *cause* for this discontent, and the readiness to form acquaintances with strangers without proper introductions or the consent of parents; basically it is similar to that of the perverted youth.

Parents live a life of legalized prostitution; the mother consents to the husband's request because she desires his support, clothing, luxury and home. In innumerable cases there is no love between them and the marriage is one of convenience or selfishness.

On his part, he gives because she demands it, or by reason that he has been taught it is his duty. On her part, she chooses the easier way by selling herself for the comforts it brings her, or perhaps because she wishes to avoid the scandal of a divorce.

Whether it is the fault of one or the other, or both, the fact cannot be denied or contradicted that the marriage rite is desecrated, and either one or both prostitute a Divine function for selfish purposes. Where there is a lack of love or affection it is prostitution, even if the indulging pair are legally wedded, and all too frequently the results are unwanted children.

These are *unfortunately born;* not having been conceived in love—holiness—consequently *without an inborn love for the pure and good;* naturally dissatisfied and more often than not, with an insatiable longing for all that is unattainable in the home environment.

There is no Soul, or spiritual desire in the heart for the real, lasting things of life, consequently no resisting force against the wiles of wolves in sheep's clothing. This is not even the worst feature in these cases; the children conceived in passion, undesired and cursed because of lack of love before birth, seldom, if ever, *receive the proper care and correct training.* Who can blame them if they become scarlet women? Our pity, as is God's, should be with them.

We maintain: Assuming man and wife love each other, possess a longing for children to bless their home, have a correct knowledge of creative laws, these becoming parents to a girl, and instructing her thoroughly and without false modesty, in chaste language, *would never need to fear any white slaver, however seductive his talk and glittering his promises.*

Why?

Because a girl thus born and instructed would not form acquaintances without informing her parents; nor would she consent to any arrangements without her parents' approval. Should such an one be abducted, no force in the universe could induce her to commit, or consent to, wrong; honor being dearer to her than life itself.

Where shall we seek the remedy for these great evils, and by applying it, save the race? Shall we punish the guilty ones, the white slavers and their cohorts, as is the common practice these days, and stop there? This procedure is necessary, but is insufficient; like all local remedies, it treats the effect, leaving the cause operative.

We must remove the cause by fully instructing the present and coming generations in the entire *laws of being;* likewise teaching parents all that concerns the procreative organism; by offering a true knowledge of cause and effect, and the absolute and unrevokable edict that "the Soul that sinneth, it shall die," no force in the universe being available to set the law aside or revoke the penalty when deserved.

The girl rightly born and correctly taught will never open the way for anyone to betray her; this is her true salvation and protection; while the boy lovingly conceived and instructed in the laws governing manhood will never entice or degrade womanhood. Meanness and perversion unborn in the heart of boys cannot manifest in their future relationship with their mates.

There is no acceptable excuse for the criminal ignorance pervading humanity concerning the abuses of the generative and regenerative faculties and forces. No longer will we be permitted to plead as an excuse that it is irreligious to instruct our children in these subjects, because of fear that they may make unholy use of the knowledge. On the contrary, it has *now become a holy religious duty to instruct the children, clear-*

ly and convincingly, inculcating the truth that for the Soul to be saved, only Divine use, (through, and in love) *may be made of the creative function, and that to "cast the seed to Moloch," or exchange, when lust is the incentive of action, is to damn the body, mind, and finally, the Soul itself.*

Every boy and girl able to read will find in any daily paper more degrading information in the scandals paraded before the public than could possibly be contained in the entire exposition of sex and its laws, when clothed in sane and chaste language.

We constantly permit our children to read scandal mongering sheets, while persistently refusing to enlighten them respecting the creative functions; refusing to permit their instruction in the correct knowledge that they may know how to preserve their honor and purity and guard themselves against the pitfalls and snares, disease, sorrow and misery resulting from the abuse of these functions.

Surely, we must admit that it is far more desirable and noble to teach the prevention of wrong than to punish our children for the immorality of which they may become guilty and from which we might have saved them.

Who are those sitting in judgment, issuing edicts that we shall not teach the saving truth? With rare exception they are those who themselves abused their procreative functions to an extent resulting in incompetence; consequently their action is governed by their knowledge of the dark, disgusting, degrading aspect, and by their total ignorance of the elevating, reconstructive, regenerating feature.

Another class ready to taboo the entire subject are those of cold, frigid, forbidding temperament, who cannot see aught but wrong in the nature that is warm, sensitive, loving, normal, therefore passionate, *as the great Creator intended.*

A great awakening is due; an enlightenment among mankind generally to the goodness, purity, and nobleness of the exalted creative function; to be utilized for the betterment of man; rather than employed for his degradation. An appreciation of the fact that if the race is to be redeemed, prompt action is essential, otherwise the universal fountain of life will become so weakened that cleansing and strengthening will have become utterly impossible.

One reason so many good men and women avoid knowledge pertaining to sex and its functions is because for so many centuries they have been deluded with the idea, inculcated by church and state, that the creative organism has no other purpose than procreation and pleasure, with pleasure designated as sinful. Even now, they as yet cannot comprehend the deeper and holier significance and exercise of the function. They cannot bring themselves to a realization of the uncontradictable fact that any one may be pure in thought or intention who deliberately seeks a frank discussion of the sex question; nor are they as yet awake to the birth of a new age as regards this problem.

Whereas, sex has been the means for carnal pleasure first, and procreation last—an incident rather than an intent, for the most part—it is henceforth to become the symbol of the *procreation of desired, longed-for, and welcomed children and for regeneration of both body and Soul, founded upon a basis of mutual love.* No longer should it be considered the carnal and degrading act that would shame the lowest brute, not to mention the all-wise Father who created the sexes for holy purposes, and, looking upon His work, saw "that all was good."

The sooner mankind can be awakened to a full realization of the new understanding—the earlier can we convince the more intelligent classes among whom honor still exists—the quicker shall we be able to start the new race marching onward toward greater achievements, purer lives, and a truer and nobler manhood and womanhood.

WHERE TO BEGIN?—that's the question.

Undoubtedly, the initiative should be taken on the side of the daughter; and the proper time is the moment she is capable of asking questions; inquiry clearly indicating thought on a subject which is a mystery to her.

She must be instructed, made to understand and *believe* that she is God's most beautiful, noble and sacred handiwork; that with her is the responsibility of restoring the race to its primitive purity, with an exalted personality. All that concerns her must be explained: why she is a woman, for what purpose she is here, how she must guard and protect herself; that above all else she must not permit liberties to be taken, yet must remain normal and natural, a delightful companion, a good partner, and in all affairs demand respect for herself and her creative potentialities.

She must be instructed in her duties, as well as the rights of man; what she may demand, as well as what may be rightly demanded or requested of her, and to what extent she should comply. She must be fully taught the power that resides in her department of creation and how she must employ this power in the commencement of the beginning of a superior race.

In short, she must come to a thorough comprehension of the glory of her being; likewise an understanding of her weakness that she may the better guard herself against others seeking to take advantage of her.

Let us save the girl by teaching her how to protect herself, never lowering herself for any reason whatsoever. In redeemed and glorified womanhood lies emancipation of the race from degradation, savagery, war and misery. *The womb of woman is God's exalted laboratory wherein mankind is fashioned. When we elevate womanhood, we also promote the incentive for the development of a superior race.*

One of the great moral cancers eating out the heart of mankind is the almost universal practice of promiscuous sex relationship. Arriving at a period of time when it shall be the exception, rather than the rule, for men to seek carnal intercourse with more than one woman, we will have advanced far toward freeing humanity from the *internal inferno* that is consuming it.

The man who has lived a normal life for years, but because of the continued coldness of his wife, forgets the moral code and looks with favor upon another woman, especially the woman "for sale" at once fills his blood with a fire no water can quench. If he is foolish enough to return to his wife and indulge in sexual congress, he will inoculate her with the virus; should children result from such a union, they also may be consumed with unsatisfiable desire. Is there need to wonder why we so seldom see a normal boy or girl, considering that almost the entire world is filled with this unholy fire.

The greatest crime man can commit against himself and his progeny is to seek sexual embrace with more than one woman within a limited time; yet it is an even greater crime for woman to do so, because she absorbs directly into her blood stream the various fires which act as would chemicals not in affinity, when placed in a retort.

We wish it distinctly understood that we do not make this statement, or even indicate, that all men are unfaithful to the one woman, whether wife or sweetheart, or that all women are generally unfaithful, even in thought, to their husbands. We have reference only to that vast army of men and women who find nothing sacred in sex and who constantly seek carnal pleasure at the expense of humankind and in defiance of God's fiat.

If it is impossible for a man to arouse the passions of his wife through caresses and other natural means so that compliance to his wishes is willingly granted, he should not even attempt to coerce her, because it would be a form of legalized rape. If, unable to control his desires, he seeks the embrace of another woman, he must not, under any circumstances, while such an unhallowed relationship continues, have aught to do with his wife; to disobey this law is to follow the Path of Death.

For a woman, the dire consequences of attempting to harmonize two or more forces is far more disastrous than it is for a man, because the contamination resulting from trying to serve husband and lover is more direct and lasting.

Many moral and honest men, during a moment of forgetfulness, allow themselves to be led astray, by friend or passion. Thereafter they find all their thoughts, opinions and ideas changed. They become discontented with conditions which formerly satisfied them; yet unable to comprehend the cause for the dissatisfaction and irritation which may become great enough to part them from the woman they loved.

Similarly, the woman who, in a moment of injured pride, pique, or through intercession of a "good friend," side-steps the straight and narrow path, engenders a fever within herself that destroys peace of heart and mind, and often causes her ultimate downfall.

CONTINENCE IN THE MARRIED

Countenanced Neither by Nature Nor by God

THE CREATOR, Jehovah, made no mistake in the manner of His creations, nor in the Laws He established for their government. To even think that He instituted a department of life, established Laws for its welfare and continuance, and then annulled them, is to accuse the Maker of both ignorance and indecision, and to impute to Him all of the weaknesses possessed by His creatures.

Man was created by the wisdom of the Creator; male and female created He them. As in all things in Nature, there is a duality here; a balance or equilibrium. A one-sided condition cannot exist. His plans for the human race permitted of no errors and man cannot improve upon the laws instituted for his guidance and development.

Granting that God created the sexes, the argument is advanced that He intended the exercise of the sex function to be solely for the purpose of procreation. Such an argument is illogical and unworthy of a sane, sensible mind.

Nature is dual, an incontrovertible fact, as all her methods and workings of the laws prove. God's plan regarding sex also is dual—dual both in form and purpose. The pendulum swings with equal precision both ways.

The opposite of the male is the female; of generation, REgeneration; of procreation, REcreation of the self—the Biblical "ye must be born again."

In simple terms, through the exercise of the sex function,

by generation, is brought about the propagation of the race, or the creating of life in another body; through sex, by *re-generation* is developed the life "more abundant" in the self-body. Therefore, sex is as indispensable and necessary to the individual as it is to the race.

The welfare, growth, and unfoldment of the individual is in exact ratio to the importance of populating the earth. Continence has no status in the Law of Life.

If sex activity is a violation of the Law of God, then all those who disobey that law must suffer the penalty. (We are now dealing with the normal man and woman, not perverts.) It is beyond dispute that men living in harmony with the law reap the benefits of their obedience.

For example: Men working in conjunction with the law governing the physical body possess health; those planning and working in harmony with the law of prosperity have wealth and possession and so on *ad infinitum. The greater the harmony between God and His children,* the more of good is bestowed upon man.

If non-use is the law of sex, then the comparatively few unmarried men and women of absolute chastity come under the bounty of the law; being "perfect in the law" they should, and would be, gods and goddesses in greatness of power, beauty of person, and advanced in development, not to mention the vivacity and sweetness of disposition.

Do facts manifest this? Do any of the adherents of continence possess these desirable qualifications? Do we not more often find the approach to these characteristics in the happily married of much mutual embrace (so admitted by them), than in the unmarried?

Facing fairly without evasion this important question, one must admit that the followers of sex-continence almost universally exemplify unfortunate traits and most undesirable weaknesses.[1]

All too many people, otherwise intelligent, sincerely believe and argue that as animals co-habit only for the perpetuation of their species, men, also, should be satisfied by imitating the creatures of the woods and fields and depend upon evolutionary activity alone for their development.

We could as sensibly argue that the instincts and propensities of the horse or cow, or even the swine, should serve man as an example to the spiritually awakened, as to compare the demands and requirements of the animal nature or plant life to those of the spiritually awakened and developing human beings.

Nature has perfectly adjusted the requirements of animal and plant kingdoms to the laws of those realms. The line of demarcation between man and beast is distinctly drawn and an equal distinction exists in the laws governing them. Men are supposed to live in harmony with God, which includes all other harmonies. Animals and plants live in conformity with the purpose of nature; whose one and only great incentive is the reproduction of their species; resultantly, the exercise of the creative function takes place only when this is possible. Dominated by the law of her being, the female animal consents, and conception occurs only while she is in season.

When the lunar period is past, she refuses all advances of the male, fighting if need be, to free herself of these attentions.

---

[1] We have in mind only the modern self-styled philosophical and religious-spiritual organizations who teach continence to their fellows and either practice the contrary or prove guilty of the worst forms of sex debasement.

This attitude is in conformity with the laws governing animals and in no way applies to higher beings.

Possessing only the lower nature, the animal has no possibility of re-generation, consequently, there is neither call nor reason for sex activity, except for reproduction.

Human beings are governed by an entirely different law. Woman does not conceive during the lunar season, but just before or shortly after. We do not say that conception would not take place during that period, or that it cannot, *but we maintain it should not.*

To conceive during this period is a crime against the Creator of the sexes, against the woman who consents or suffers it to occur, and against the child to be born under such a condition. The result of conception during the lunar season is always undesirable; an instance of this is the Biblical story of Jacob and Esau.

There is as much difference in the law governing the demonstration of sex, between the human and the animal, as there is in the matter of clothing or covering, or in the kind and preparation of food. It is not only irrational, but criminal as well, to exalt the animal kingdom as an example for the human.

There are as many reasons against the practice of continence, as there are tones in the musical scale. We state here the most obvious, physical one. It is immaterial what the man's work may be, whether fatiguing bodily labor or nerve-exhausting study, or how gross or spiritual his employment or vocation, how little he thinks or how philosophically; the body is a laboratory continuously refining the seminal fluid and storing it for use. Sooner or later this fluid, which could more correctly be termed an "elixir," must be used or disposed of.

We employ the words "used" and "disposed" advisedly. They express our exact meaning. Take the highest form of life which man is capable of living; the man of superior wisdom; one with a divine understanding of the laws of God, and who, through this knowledge, knows how to use the seminal fluid for the REgeneration of the self, his body. Even in his case, there will be a surplus, and if this is not absorbed in a natural manner, it must eliminated from the system, by the urine, nocturnal emission, or otherwise.

If allowed to remain in the body unabsorbed, it becomes stagnant and therefore poisonous to the system; what is more and worse, it has a destructive effect on the cellular tissue of the brain, and the powers of Will and discrimination are adversely influenced.

This often results in perversion and ends in self-degradation. Physical and mental health demands that the seminal fluids not used for creative purposes should be turned into other channels—that of REgeneration and in renewing life and strength.

The higher the understanding a man has of the possibilities, potentialities and destinies of the human race, the loftier will be his conception of the *powers, forces and possibilities* of the individual.

Conclusions are based on a true foundation when man admits that he was created with a powerful sex nature to be used in *wise* and *holy* activities. To limit that application or direction by confining its action to the purpose of reproduction alone is unnatural to his dual—human and spiritual—nature, and frequently leads to degeneracy.

The laws of God and nature do not limit man except to confine him within the bounds of natural and spiritual laws.

The seminal fluid is created abundantly by the system, and though a man were to live more or less a polygamous life, and in addition, use up all that was necessary in the recreation and renewing of his own body, the secretions would exceed his requirements.

There are many, most of them spiritually debased by their own secret practices, who loudly deplore the "commonness" of the sex impulse and emphasize the sordid physical side; claiming they are repulsed by it and that at best it is to be exercised only for cohabitation.

Thus do they try to besmirch one of God's greatest blessings —the means of both generation and REgeneration—and turn it into a curse or a calamity.

These are the same people, usually, who are "too nice" to admit to their children that child-birth is both natural and normal, as well as sacred. They prefer to tell them tales of babies being brought by the stork, by the doctor in his little bag, or by angels from heaven, all of which the children already know are falsehoods, hence the parents are considered as fabricators and not to be trusted when truth is wanted or desired.

Our assertion that continence is *not* sanctioned by God is based on truth and cannot be successfully contradicted. We must accept the laws of God and Nature. We are no longer living in an age of fools and delusionists. It is beyond the comprehension of the thinking man and woman how any one can argue that *anything in the realm of law and order, God's world,* requires an apology. There is nothing to be ashamed of, nothing that can possibly be successfully hidden.

All Divine law, and the action thereof, is noble and beautiful. The old conceptions and feelings of shame must be abandoned. All that God has created is noble, good and holy, *unless we make it ignoble by abuse.*

The fiat of God, the laws governing sex life, creation and recreation, cannot be nullified by man. They may be perverted, degraded, and, in our blindness, we may try to set them aside, *but time finally adjusts the equilibrium; right ultimately prevails.* The creative laws of God are mightier than the beliefs, established customs or religious teachings of those who never passed the barriers of the carnal life, hence know nothing of the REgenerative life, its laws or blessings.

Institutions, man-made laws and usages, public opinion and Dame Grundy have done their best to dig a pit and bury this important subject of sex. Whether one practiced continence or not was of little moment, so long as the matter was not discussed. Whether right or wrong, let the advocates of continence teach it if they like, so long as it was not taught *en masse,* or openly contradicted.

Silence and ignorance were considered virtues. *The subject will not down.* We can no longer keep silent; *we who know the truth must proclaim it.*

The diseases, mental and physical, arising from an adherence to continence, formerly laid to other doors, must now be recognized as the legitimate outgrowth of a perverted law, and on a par with debased and degenerate acts.

All through the ages this ugly monster, continence, has shown its head. Wherever it has trailed its hideous body, it has left in its wake the most degraded forms of perversion and degradation. All the crimes in the category of evil have followed.

The natural use of a part or function produces natural

results. The perverted use of an organism or function produces undesirable conditions and destructive consequences. Health, saneness, mental and physical equilibrium, all these blessings are the natural lot of those living in harmony with sex laws. We can, *and do,* find the opposites of these blessings among the followers of continence.

Why this senseless discrimination against certain parts of the body? The food eaten by man is digested, assimilated, and the residue naturally eliminated. This is anything but an esthetic process, but nothing is thought of it; it has always been an open subject; consideration of it never thought degrading.

In *fact,* there is no difference between the laws governing the functions of creation and those of digestion, absorption and elimination. Only because of secrecy is this part of the body considered ignoble and something of which to be ashamed. The comparison of the different functions is not unappropriate; health reduced to its simplest terms depends upon secretions being assimilated and the elimination of all surplus.

Do we stretch a point when we say the physical law acts in exactly the same way, whether it is a colon to be evacuated or a gland to be relieved? We think not. In either case, suppression or retention is injurious.

If for any reason the bowels do not perform properly, we do not hesitate to ask a physician's advice for treatment. There are men and women trained to teach and advise in sex matters. Why consult a doctor about one and ignore the other, the more important one?

Is there much, if any, difference in the reason and principle of elimination as manifested by the various organs of the body? Food is received into the stomach and reduced to a form essential for its assimilation and the rebuilding of the bodily structure. It is taken up by the blood, oxidized in the lungs, and rebuilds bone, muscle, nerve and flesh.

Waste passes out of the system through the various organs of elimination, not only through one. The bowels, kidneys, lungs, skin and sex organs all assist nature. Is it sane or reasonable to disqualify any one of these because of an aversion due to ignorance, shame or guilt?

If the bowels refuse to function properly, constipation follows; there is a consequent poisoning of the system, termed "autointoxication,"[2] or self-poisoning. Disease, ultimately producing death, results unless we remove the cause so that the intestines again perform their normal work.

If a man consciously ignores this physical law and if disease, and finally death, claims him, is he not a suicide? God's law is *cause* and *effect;* man refuses to assist the bowels to movement; that is cause. Death is the logical effect.

The Creator is not concerned as to how we circumvent His laws, or what methods we employ; the penalty is always the same; unfailingly certain.

When we are not in harmony with law, we reap disaster. A man is guilty of suicide whether he swallows poison, shoots himself, or refuses to aid a diseased bowel. Before the great Lawgiver these various infractions bring about the same results; all are equally effectual in bringing about disaster.

If the kidneys do not perform their functions properly, illness results. Bright's disease or some other malady makes itself manifest; the indication that they are not functioning

---

[2] "Autointoxication" is an abused term. Reabsorption of poisonous material should be known as "Toxo-absorption." See *Diet, The Key to Health*. Philosophical Publishing Company, Quakertown, Penna.

according to the law governing them. If remedies are not applied, death is certain. If the lungs are not performing their duty, they weaken gradually, tubercular indications appear and death is merely a question of time.

The law governing is identical in every part of the elimina-tive system. All these organs receive a share of the nutriment from the food ingested. It is apportioned to them according to their requirements for the rebuilding and keeping in repair of their particular organism.

All that is not used in construction and reconstruction is refuse and *must be eliminated, otherwise it will deteriorate, induce irritation and finally destroy. This is the law.*

The law of elimination applies equally to all the eliminative processes of the body. From the nutriment furnished the body the sex organism selects its own portion. It cannot appropriate every particle of it any more than can the intestines or kidneys. In every department of construction and repair there is waste; *this must be discarded one way or another.*

If the unwholesome, insanitary, contrary-to-law idea of con-tinence is followed and the waste retained, it is thrown back into the general system as a congestant and positive poison, which ultimately induces a disease and may be the cause of death.

The pathological effect of various infections produce differ-ent diseases in the body; that is, the action of poisons secreted by the different organs produce numerous ailments.

The effect of a diseased kidney is not unlike that of a con-gested liver; though the disease of the kidneys has a direct influence on the sex organism, because the kidneys were an-ciently believed to be the Biblical "reins," wherein the *seminal fluid is produced.*

The infection due to stagnant seminal fluid is far-reaching and elusive; the poison thus generated not merely affects the bodily tissues, but through the blood and nervous systems attacks the centers of mental activity and the same form of neurosis may result. The reasoning faculties and the moral nature surrender to this insidious taint.

The imbecile and the pervert are extreme examples; but the world is full of other victims inoculated with mental and physical infection. Onanism, Sodomism, so named after the Biblical Sodom Gomorrahism, and the specialized houses in the red-light districts of the larger cities are proof of this. Can any one doubt the necessity of scientific and philosophical instructions on this subject?

The adherents of continence declare that love is the prevention and the cure of disease, whether of the sex nature or of any other part of the body. The divinity of love is a cure, but the man or woman living in disobedience to God and His laws is not in a position to talk of or apply the principles of love in its higher aspects.

We enter a protest against such a man or woman using the word love. They do not possess the slightest concept of its meaning. Love and sex are the dual parts of the emotional nature; there can be no true, lasting love without vigorous sex. *The strength of a man's love equals the virility of his sex power.*

Is it possible for a man to love a woman, who through bad habits or abuse has deprived himself of "manly strength?" *Emphatically no!* Love, as experienced by incarnated beings, cannot be divorced from the alchemy of sex. A man may be mentally faithful to the woman, but that is not love.

Go farther. Is it possible for him to love father, mother,

brothers and sisters, in the truest sense of the word? Again we repeat *no*. If he is not an all-around *man* he is not in possession of the prerogatives of man.

Follow this question to the ultimate. Is it possible for him to truly love God? The answer is the likewise emphatic "NO." To truly love is to love wholly (holy), with all of one's nature as a unit.

The diseased or subnormal man is not whole; half of his emotional nature is weak or neurotic, and half a man cannot give a whole man's love to either woman or God.

All the famous men and women who have become great in the world of action and accomplishment were those possessing fully developed, normal sex natures. Proven celibates and eunuchs are not listed among the Immortals. If there was ever any misuse of the sex function by famous men and women it was on the side of super-activity, never non-use.

It is utterly impossible for a man to be healthy, virile and strong, capable of physical and mental activity along any line of the world's work, who does not attend to the organs of elimination in his own body. Neither is it possible for a man to be healthy in body and mind, full of strength and vivacity, who does not live a natural life. The man who is love-starved, system-congested, mind-poisoned has little chance of success or happiness.

The so-called doctrine of continence may be likened to a pool of water surrounded by a wall of masonry. The fresh water pours into the basin which, when filled, automatically shuts off the inflow. From that time on, only an amount of water equal to the quantity soaking away or evaporating finds its way into the pool. What is the result? A child could guess the answer. *Stagnation.*

The life and the purity of the water depends upon an outlet, or outflow of the water already in the pool, and an inflow of fresh water—on circulation and aeriation. If this is interfered with, the stagnation generates poisons and each particle seeking its affinity, rises to the top of the pool, unites itself with virulent matter already there and forms a poisonous film over the body of water.

As the pool of water requires an inflow of fresh water to keep it pure and wholesome, so does the creative organism of man need a constant inflow of the vital fluids. This presupposes an outlet or outflow. This outlet denied, nature seizes other means of protecting her interests. Continence is a deliberate closing of the outlet, consequently there is room for only an infinitesmal amount of the fresh vital fluids, the organism already being congested.

The result is stagnation of the seminal fluids in the creative organism. Stagnation always is creative of poisons. Poison created or generated in the congested area, finds its way into the circulation, affecting all the tissues of the body.

This is ultimately followed by a disturbed equilibrium affecting the entire system of man; undermining his moral nature, deadening his spiritual conscience; weakening the Will; and, as a result of irritation, giving impetus to increased desire. The natural, normal outlet being closed, creative nature turns upon the one guilty.

Perversions of many kinds and a thousand evils come into existence under self-imposed, reasonless continence. The mentality gradually weakens, the Will loses its power and man becomes a helpless victim of himself—all under the delusion that he is treading the path to spirituality.

CONTINENCE

An Individual Problem

THE problem of sex, like that of dietetics, is an individual one. Men differ from one another in their requirements. While different foods are necessary for different types of people, the general laws governing nutrition apply to the race as a whole. It is the same with the laws governing the creative function. These also have a general application; but the individual activity *must be in harmony with the Law.*

Some men store up an immense reserve of vital force. Even though more than the normal amount of vitality is expended in business and life in general, there is still a surplus that must be directed along other avenues. The most important outlet is by means of *the marital rite in exchange* for other forces so essential to mental and physical well-being. The unmarried naturally require a different method.

That Race REgeneration may be made certain, the laws of both God and nature, as they concern man's advancement physically, mentally AND SPIRITUALLY, must be fully understood *and obeyed.* Preconceived ideas must be exchanged for actual knowledge. Truth alone is acceptable as a guide.

This enigma of sex is one of the most important of all of man's problems, both individually and nationally, aye, universally. In married life normal marital relationship between man and wife is not only essential to the health of body and mind for the individuals directly concerned, but equally so for the procreation of a healthy, normal and symmetrically developed progeny, and hence important to the race of the future.

It is not possible for a man, after indulging in the marital rite for a considerable length of time, then, whether of his own free will or due to conditions over which he has no control, to live the continent life for a time and again return to the marital rite with the same degree of satisfaction as before. And why not?

Beginning with adolescence and continuing until Menopause, the creative laboratory (of the "seed" or spermatozoon) is *continually* active. The "seed" which is being constantly created or manufactured by this great laboratory is used not alone for the creation of new beings, as so many believe, or in exchange with the mate during the marital rite for the physical, mental and spiritual being, but also for the *re*building of the self; the "seed" germs or spermatozoon often present in the marrow of the bones and in other parts of the body.

This laboratory is constantly active in manufacturing vital forces and if man, as a result of some mistaken notion, discontinues to furnish an outlet for these forces or seals up this "fountain of youth;" (it being recognized that this laboratory discontinues functioning at the end of youth), and if man refuses to keep the seminal fluid or vital forces in circulation, a form of stagnation sets in which acts adversely upon the entire being of the guilty one. To remain healthy and normal, it is essential that man's reproductive organism be kept active by normal, natural use. We still have the married in mind.

What of the feminine side of this important problem? In a medical practice of more than forty years, with experience in almost every part of the world and in the treatment of many thousands of women, we have never found a truly normal, healthy woman, whose husband had become a foolish victim to the belief of continence if she also practiced continence. Without exception, the organism of the woman's generative system was diseased in one manner or another. Misplacement of the uterus, inflamed or congested ovaries and ulcerated cervix with Leucorrhea, were only part of her ailments.

The practice of continence among the married not only produces sexual weakness and *de*moralizes the man, but also curses the woman with untold ills.[1]

The man who persists in this unlawful (Biblically) practice will find a gradual decline in his general ability. His mind becomes less keen; there is inability to analyze minutely. He loses the incentive to plan and act, becoming mentally negative. Physically he soon drops below par; shortly nursing headaches; becoming nervous and irritable and acquires digestive weaknesses. With the suppression of sex activity there also appears a general inertia and the development of neurasthenic tendencies.

Such undesirable effects are only the beginning of the curses that trail in the wake of this destructive practice. Following the weakness of the mental faculties and the general inertia of the body, comes the debilitating influence on the power of reason and Will; culminating in the gradual disintegration of moral stamina. Such a condition is only one step removed from sex perversion.

Possibly the most heart-rending confessions to which we are continually forced to listen come from those men, many

---

[1] There are countless instances where, due to the illness of husband and wife, continence for more or less lengthy periods are necessary. In these instances a powerful psychological factor enters, but even so, there are penalties to be paid for the infractions of a positive Law.

still in their youth, who, through well-meaning intentions or modern Onanistic preachments, have attempted to live the continent life, only to find that when they finally awoke to their duties as husbands, they found themselves so weakened that they were unable to even commence performing their duties.

What was the natural consequence? A disillusioned wife either accusing her mate of expending his *manly* strength with some other woman, or seeking a lover capable of making up for the weakness displayed by the man whose *duty* and *desire* it should have been to love and *embrace* her.

The sex exercise of man is a natural function. Contrary to the same function and its exhibition in the animal, it is not alone for procreation, but for *the regeneration of the whole man, mental and physical,* as well as for the regeneration of his mate and companion. The great Creator had this in view when He gave man a woman as his daily companion.

To single out conclusive proof (that sexual exercise was not intended for one purpose only) from the mass of contradictory arguments and teachings, is not at all difficult.

Contrast the inclinations of the human with the animal. In the lower order, where instinct rules, rather than thought and the *capacity to plan,* the female seeks the male (note this law carefully) during her lunar season. At no other time does she indicate mating desire; nor does the male recognize her existence, as a female, before or after that period.

Had He who created men and animals established the identical laws to govern both alike, why did He implant in the two, separate creative instincts respecting the same function?

Why are animal and human inclinations radically and fundamentally different? Why is coition during the lunar period sought by the animal female, and absolutely repugnant to the human female?

As already noted, the female animal desires cohabitation *during* the season of reproduction; the male is attracted to her, and sought out by her, at this special time.

It is radically different with the woman, the opposite in every respect; unclean during this period, the time of the menstrual flow, she is passive; normally the idea of embrace repulses her; if caresses awaken her desires she yet refuses all advances, unless she has become one of the rapidly increasing number of perverts. Should she desire conjugal exercise and should she conceive during the time of her uncleanliness, the result is a child marked in one way or another.

Unlike the animal, except in extraordinary cases, the woman exhibits affection and desire after, not during, her hours of abstinence. As a general rule, if she conceives shortly after this period, a strong child should be the result; and it may be stated in passing, that the greater the passion—love being one of the aspects of her desire—the stronger and more virile will be the offspring.

The possibility of conception decreases with the passing of the days following the moon's phase. After ten days there is a constantly lessening possibility of pregnancy; and it is not likely that she will be able to conceive until a day or so before the actual commencement of the next period.

Should conception result during the pre-lunar season, the child is liable to be deficient in vital force; the life-sex-energy stored up in the mother from the previous purification having become depleted and thus prohibiting her from bequeathing the full vitality which she herself does not possess.

There are, as a general rule, a certain number of days each month during which most women are incapable of conceiving, hence reproduction is impossible. Nevertheless, a woman may, during this period, greatly desire the conjugal embrace. If the laws of the animal world were given for the guidance of the human race, why was the mother of the race granted approximately fourteen sacred "open days" wherein free indulgence is not denied her? It is significant to note that the moment a female animal desires, she seeks satisfaction.

If continence is a sound doctrine, why should the female of our specie be filled with unsatisfied longing more than one-half of her time? *Revealed* religion has enlightened God's children that during this time man (and woman through him) may contact the inhabitants of the Stellar spaces, and receive strength and wisdom for his guidance.[1]

It is apparent to all but the ignorant and narrow zealot that for man God instituted a wholly different creative and re-creative law, than that for the animal. Men and women *do* find strength, health, *renewal of youth,* peace of mind and *greater love,* together with all powers and blessings, through obedience to the law of *correct* use. Sexual exercise is a source of incentive in both thought and action; the stronger the virility, the greater the potentiality for achievement; it is the source of health, of happiness, and of all the benefits that belong to life.

When we speak in this broad emphatic manner, we have in mind rational indulgence, *not* license. Normal exercise

---

[1] See *Eulis,* Philosophical Publishing Company, Quakertown, Penna.

and license are as far apart as the poles of the earth. One induces health, well-being and the possibility of success; the other is an incitant to disease, morbidness, perversion (quite often), and the destruction of all that is good, ending usually in an ignoble death.

The sensual desire should be controlled in the same manner as should all other appetites. A wise man eats only sufficiently to supply the requirements of the physical being. Too much food congests the entire system, producing the very opposite of the effect desired. The exercise of the creative function must be only to the degree conducive to health and vitality; a normal satisfaction always resulting in peace and contentment.

The question of temperament is of vast importance in dealing with the issue under consideration. Race REgeneration cannot become a science until we understand individual dispositions, and the good and bad characteristic combinations. Ignorance of the requirements of different temperaments is productive of sin and suffering. The mating of natures is quite as important a problem as the mating of bodies.

For example: A man of vital temperament, full of virility and force, ought never to marry a woman of a cold, unimaginative, phlegmatic nature. Such a union will make of existence a hell for both, and the children of the union are certain to be deficient mentally, and frequently afflicted with some physical weakness.

Careful selection of a fitting mate is of prime importance; race development depends upon right selection. A normal child can be expected only when pleasure, peace of mind and complete satisfaction attend the marriage rite and that is impossible where the twain are improperly mated.

As abnormal children often result through the mating of virile fathers and cold mothers, so also do they appear when the mother desires the embrace of the father twice a week, in harmony with the rules of Solomon, and is reluctantly granted the embrace once a fortnight.   Here is such an instance:

Only a week before the foregoing paragraph was written, a woman, one whom we had cared for during a severe nervous affliction, now the mother of two children, and *enceinte* with the third, confessed to us that her severe attacks of nervous irritation, amounting to irrational action, were the direct result of a continuous desire for the embrace; this being granted her possibly once a week, or every two weeks, *then only at her own request.*   What will be the result of such a conception? Has any man the right to become a father, who cannot, or will not (as in this case), righteously support the mother-to-be.

The teaching of, and obedience to, the doctrine of continence, will never regulate the tendencies of the age, nor succeed in reforming them.   Quite the opposite; by the practice of such delusive instructions the very things we wish to regulate, or annihilate, are certain to become more firmly established.

Continence is, in itself, a form of perversion; only in the rarest instances can a man begin living the continent life without showing signs of weakness, nervousness, and, were he to confess the truth (many have), they would include mental distortions—the thoughts and imaginings leading to perversion. This is the first stage of deterioration; the second follows close on its heels; negation of all love, selfishness and, finally, degradation.

A normal *unsatisfied* appetite incites to a perversion of that desire *without a single exception.*   Suppression of any natural longing, power or potency has never been a success and never can be. *Nothing dies.* When an attempt is made to suppress or destroy a normal tendency, we merely hold it in check for a limited time until a change has taken place in its activity and then, in some disguise, it manifests in a new sphere.

There is nothing higher on the physical plane than the normal; if it changes its material form, shape, or design, it becomes abnormal. Consequently, if a normal sex power is suppressed it becomes unnatural, the first step on the path to perversion.

Men, practicing continence, have been heard to justify their action by voicing the sentiment that if all men were like them, the red light districts in towns and cities would soon be extinct. This is seemingly true; but hides an untruth. It is *not* the men of normal sex practices that give life and support to vice, but those guilty of attempting to suppress normal desire, and those in an environment of life where normal action is denied them.

Thousands of men are starved in their love-expression because of the ignorance of their wives. These women have been taught that sex is degrading; that to acknowledge passion in themselves is a shameful admission. They discourage the sacred relationship, and the husbands, if normal, seek relief and understanding elsewhere—usually among the undesirables of the city's population, because *they have too much respect and manhood to approach a girl or woman to whom they cannot offer honorable marriage in exchange for the favor.*

Such women destroy their own love-nature and change what should be a happy home, into a mere lodging house; all because they deem themselves purer and holier than the Creator who made them to love and express their sex nature; giving them an organism wonderfully constructed for that purpose, but which they "bury," as did the Biblical character his talents.

There are countless men and women (some of them may possibly peruse these pages) who pride themselves on being adherents to the doctrine of continence, and why?   Because, for one reason or another, *they cannot be otherwise.*   They have expended their "inheritance" in riotous living.   They have lost health, strength, and even desire; their "Divine" laboratory has ceased functioning.   Of these, God has said: "the Soul that sinneth, it shall die."

There are narrow minded, bigoted men and women who, because of some bitter experience in life, have frozen every particle of heart and Soul out of themselves.   They cannot love; all warmth has departed; they have lost all power of conjugal affection.   They are often termed "vinegary-faced" and deserve the appellation; but these are to be deeply pitied.

Another class, capable of continence in the accepted meaning of the term, are neurotics and victims of religious excitement who haunt revival meetings.   These are generally sexually diseased, and while in a state of hysteria, often unknown to themselves, they experience the *orgasmal climax;* leaving them relaxed, weak, but satisfied of their holiness.

These same people, usually women, are loudest in their praise of continence; the purity of their life while, they are in fact, the victims of self-satisfaction (unconscious self-abuse) brought about by religious fervor; a condition a thousand times worse than the exercise they deplore in others.

There are numerous types of men who consider woman of use only because of her capacity to gratify their debasing lusts. These cannot be persuaded that woman has legitimate desires and a right to experience the same pleasurable sensations that they crave.

These brutes are a curse and a blasphemy on God's holy creative institutions. They exercise the function solely for their own satisfaction and, having satisfied themselves, they leave their partner in a state of feverish excitement. God has pity for the victims of such ruthless ingrates, they suffer exceedingly through no fault of their own. A continual repetition of this destructive practice results in an internal irritation; inducing, in time, an abnormal condition of the creative organism.

This tantalizing state of affairs often acts as an incentive to the purest woman living to either indulge in solitary vices or become the mistress of the first *real* male with sense enough to appreciate her. Were we to be the arbiter in passing judgment on such an one, we would free her with a blessing and imprison the brute guilty of her downfall.

Women are not the only sufferers in this respect. There are countless men, affectionate and true of heart and nature, gifted with great virility; filled with love and honor for their wives, but who have almost every natural request refused. Their sense of honor and loathing of promiscuity prevents them from seeking satisfaction outside of their own fireside. Their normal desire for conjugal embrace, remaining unsatisfied, gradually brings about an irritation of the urinary canal. The glands become congested, then inflamed and swollen, and this brings about many cases of Prostatitis; is ruinous to health and affection. It destroys what was once an honest love, a normal God-given inclination.

There is a type of woman responsible for another phase of great evil. There are many good men, married to women who seek every blessing of married life, but refuse to accept the duties of motherhood, who desire, seek and even demand sexual satisfaction. They stipulate that the husband shall be *with them* for a time, then withdraw, a practice of either *Coitus Interruptus,* or of "casting the seed upon the ground."

They have probably no knowledge of the Divine edict against "giving *any* of the seed to Moloch,"—*Lev.* 20:2. *i.e.,* the casting of the seed upon the ground in one manner or another; nevertheless they must pay the full penalty which the law exacts. Disease, dulling sensitivities, dislike and final disgust follow unfailingly. If continued, their very Souls are imperiled and a home that might have known happiness is turned into a conjugal hell.

The marital rite must be carried to a conclusion in a perfect manner. There is a right and a wrong way. No man is privileged to embrace a woman unless they both obey the sex law which God and nature instituted.

The law of reciprocity is *positive.* When the embrace is undertaken the twain must not separate until both participants are fully satisfied. When this fiat is faithfully obeyed, there is no loss of vital force by either of them. He absorbes the magnetic potency contained in her Lochia; she the vitalizing principle, the virile energy, which is the *life* of the seminal fluid. Thus is the essence of life, health and happiness exchanged between the two.

In our walks up and down the pathway of life we meet all classes. Now and then we find a woman who has passed through life without knowing either the benefits or pleasure of the sexual embrace; usually the by-product of an unfortunate love affair.

Bitterness and disappointment have turned her against love,

or any expression of it as she has learned to know it. Such women are generally rabid in their denunciation of all sex relationship; condemning everything relating to it. These women are a proof of our contention that continence affects the mentality as well as the physical being of its adherents.

There are many men who became sexually diseased early in life and then fell victims to perversions. These men have never known the embrace with a womanly woman, who, in her love, offers all. These men, become incompetent, are loudest in their belief in continence; to the contempt of all who know the reason for their opinions.

We fearlessly make the assertion: *There never was a healthy, normal, rightly-born man who had any inclination to live the continent life.* We except men fired with holy religious zeal.

God decreed: "The beauty of woman is her hair; the glory of man, his strength."

CONTINENCE

The Duality in Human Behavior

E have already said that duality is the Law of existense. It is a constant swing of the pendulum from the extreme right to the extreme left; from the extreme left to the extreme right. Without this dual activity there would be quiescence; stagnation, death. The extreme of continence is met by the opposite extreme; debauchery and libertinism; one as destructive as the other. Only *between* these two opposites can we find rationalism, naturalism and finally, divinity.

The *debauchee* and the libertine consider life worth living only in the practice of sensual excesses; only variety and promiscuity appeal to them. Like the gourmand who lives only to eat, these human beings are governed by carnality. They exist only for the enjoyment of the sensual life; they are slaves to a depraved appetite; the result of irritation and inflammation of the creative organism.

Those who preach and actually practice continence starve their entire being; body, mind and the spiritual self, because they refuse to supply their organism with the vital magnetism obtainable only through a proper exchange, and by suppression of a natural function they bring about stagnation. Those guilty of various excesses not only shock the system continually with the streams of magnetic forces from many sources, but they also counter-shock the nervous system by the different rates of vibration.

Thus they bring about irritations in the creative organism, much after the manner produced by congestion resulting from the practice of continence, and this in turn develops prostatitis and all the attendant ailments.

It is frequently questioned whether continence is as harmful to woman as it is to man and in what manner its injurious effects appear.

The basis of sex desire is widely different between the male and the female, and the results of gratification differ. Generally the desire for *Coitus* in a woman has its incentive in an entirely different emotion than that of man. In him it arises from a desire to indulge solely for pleasure's sake.

This is seldom the basis of a woman's desire. With her the act is based more on the desire to give pleasure to the loved one than her own desire for satisfaction. Woman's love or affectional nature is finer, purer and less self-interested than man's and involves different emotions.

When we say that desire for indulgence is based on pleasure or self-satisfaction, we must not forget that in health and under normal conditions there is an inner, unconscious urge *and need* for physical relief on his part, and a nervous, emotional relaxation on her part. This is an additional call of nature for the exchange of the *spirit* in the vital forces; this last being most important to health and physical well being.

The difference between the sexes is both physical and emotional. Physically, in the male there are glands which form a reservoir for the storing of highly vitalized fluids, the fluids which not only contain the "seed" for new creations, but also act as an excitant toward exercise of the function.

It is this fluid, with its "seed," which deteriorates and becomes an irritant if it is not taken into the blood circulation for the rebuilding and revitalization of the system, or exchanged during the marital embrace.

The woman possesses no such glands. She does not secrete vital fluids of this nature, but we must not overlook the fact that the vaginal glands secrete a vitalized or magnetic fluid in the lochia.

This is not an excitant, but becomes an irritant if the love and affectional nature is not satisfied as required by nature.

These physical differences are evidence that desire in woman is not based on the storing of the fluid acting as an excitant, but, as stated, on a nervous excitement called into action through the nearness and caresses of the male. Because of the lack of glands storing a vital essence, continence is not as harmful to the woman as it is to man; nevertheless, a woman practicing continence does not escape all harm—unharmed.

When the nervous system is aroused and the lochia flows freely into the vagina, it is nearly always an indication of a congestion of blood in the creative organism; and unless this congestion is relieved by the natural process of sexual embrace, the entire generative system suffers.

The destructive effects of continence appear much more quickly in man because his nature is more easily aroused, and he lacks relief because there is no release of the seminal fluid. This fluid acts as an irritant to the urinary canal, arousing a feeling of antagonism to everything about him and a morbidity concerning life as a whole.

There yet is another reason why continence is of greater harm to the male than to the female. In her, nature has fittingly established a periodic outlet for the relief and purification of the entire body, and especially the generative system.

Nature does not provide the male with any such regular source of relief. He must depend on a number of other means: involuntary losses during sleep or with the urine—not at all desirable—absorption of the vital fluids by the circulation; or *in Coitus.*

The much - mooted question as to the intensity of desire, whether the male or the female possesses the greater, cannot be answered at random or *en masse.* The balance between the sexes is preserved; but so far as individuals are concerned, it varies according to their temperament.

In the practice of many years as physician, and an equal number of years as a confessor, we have had ample opportunity to investigate this problem thoroughly and unemotionally. From the confessions of many women, we conclude the desire of the female, when thoroughly aroused by *real* love caressess is of an intensity unknown to any male. Her nervous system is infinitely finer and upon the fineness of the nerves depends the capacity to suffer or enjoy. In truth, her nervous system may be likened to the strings of the finest Opera Grand, while man's more closely resembles that of the old fashioned square piano.

Many women patients have declared without hesitation that the inflammation of the ovaries, congestion of the uterus and the abhorrent flow of *fluor albus,* are directly due to passion fully aroused but left unsatisfied.

This is so universally true that we have made it an invariable rule, in arriving at a correct diagnosis, to thoroughly question the consultant relative to her habits of sex life. In seventy-five per cent of the cases under consideration, the difficulty could be traced either to forced, partial, non-fulfillment of desire or to *Coitus Interruptus* in one form or another.

In the single, relief may be found through a change in the habits of life, and in local treatments and soothing applications. Among the married, a cure is possible if there is a mutual willingness to correct the errors of the marital embrace.

Fully fifty per cent of the sorrows, sufferings and miseries of women, whether physical, mental or domestic, or a combination of all three, are traceable to ignorance concerning matters of sex, disobedience of the laws relating to sex or resorting to unnatural practices.

The other fifty per cent coming under observation were the result of a wide variety of causes, any or all of which might accentuate the suffering due to disease of the creative organism. Under this heading might be mentioned overwork, and the consequent reaction, too-rich foods, or congestion of the system, which has a strongly adverse influence on the creative organism. In the case of girls, it has been found that dancing and other exercises performed in the company of young men, though unconscious on the part of the girls, arouses the passions and emotions and creates disturbances in the generative system.

Without fear of successful contradiction, it may be stated that while sex intensity in general may be equal in both sexes, mere passion is much more prevalent in men than in women. Men all too frequently seek the embrace as a matter of relief and pleasure, while women, as previously mentioned, become aroused sexually more through their desire to bestow pleasure on the loved one, than through the stimulus of actual physical passion.

Proof of this is readily found. A man upon becoming aroused, seeks relief—even if it is through the medium of a woman he would refuse to recognize at any other time. *This has been the curse of the human family.* A woman, on the contrary, would seldom do this. If she cannot be emotionally incited first, she remains cold to all advances; indicating that affection—not passion—is the motivating force which urges her to respond.

There are exceptions, of course, to every rule, but we have in mind the vast majority of respectable men and women. This analysis does not apply to the libertine who glories in his betrayals and *amours,* nor to the women of Scarlet Lane who seek existence through the sale of their bodies.

In discussing the problems of continence, we wish to place every phase of the subject before the student so that there will be no misunderstanding. It is admitted by all investigators that the most developed of the human race have not yet reached the ultimate of perfection in the understanding of God's Creative Laws. Our statements may appear radical, even dictatorial. We do not represent them as being final or absolute; but we do submit them as being in accordance with the findings of vast experience. We suggest that research workers weigh our assertions in the light of their own observations, maintaining an open mind, then "hold fast to that which is true."

When we contend that abstinence for any great length of time is contrary to both natural and divine law unless made necessary through absence or illness, there are certain other exceptions that must have our consideration. These exceptions all the more forcibly emphasize the truth and value of the governing law.

For example, take a normal, loving, naturally-developed woman, one who may be aroused to passion by love caresses. Suppose she chooses a husband who ultimately proves to be more brute than man; who, understanding nothing, and caring less, for the fineness and sweetness of the wife's nature, crushes her love and affection by the coarseness and brutality of his sex demonstrations; sex, to him, spelling gratification, and that only.

When he desires the exercise, he recognizes no such law as the desirability and necessity of first arousing her emotion through caresses, but acts the brute from beginning to end. To the nature of such a woman, the rite becomes a horrible nightmare. It fills her with loathing; with the result that she naturally and involuntarily remains cold and unresponsive.

If she conceives through the unnatural act, the chances will be, a hundred to one, that the child, whether male or female, will be cold by nature, utterly devoid of sex proclivities; and upon reaching adolescence, will be prone to live a continent life, because that part of the emotional and creative nature is undeveloped, if not totally missing.

Any one thus born and damned with such a constitution cannot help his or her indifference to the calls of sex; all too frequently being incapable of responding to the emotions normal to the race.

Without doubt, many of the teachers of continence who are accepted as authorities, were conceived and born under these conditions, and hence are really true to their nature. Their influence is all the more pernicious *because they are true to themselves when they teach this doctrine.* They speak from personal experience and believe their lack of desire and sex expression a normal condition, when, as an actual fact, *they are monstrosities,* born of an accursed, loveless union.

An instance in mind is that of a woman of thirty years, who, with tears of shame, sought of us the meaning of her singular attitude on sex; requesting of us an explanation of why she seemed so *different from other women.*

She confessed that she could not comprehend her own emotions, or lack of them; that never once had she desired the sexual embrace; never felt love for any man; was wholly without comprehension of the terms, "love and affection." Hearing such subjects discussed, she felt bewildered; everything belonging to the tender passion being totally beyond her comprehension.

The solution of the enigma was found through the mother. She had never once known any satisfaction. All her children were born under these conditions; were all cold of nature, sexually inert; *they lacked ambition; were without the incentive to accomplish anything in life.*

The case could be traced back to another generation; the mother being cold and unresponsive, it may well be presupposed that her mother before her had become abnormal through abuse or mismating.

Such conditions must be rectified, and a thorough knowledge of the laws governing sex is the only means through which this can be accomplished. Race regeneration cannot attain to any perceptible degree until all individuals actively express, *and manifest,* God's laws.

When every man and woman is taught the plain truth of a complete life, the reclaiming of the human race will be well on the way. What can be more sorrowful in the sight of an All-Wise Father than to see his children stumbling along in the darkness of ignorance? If man, through lack of fundamental knowledge, cannot know human love in its various aspects, *how can he ever come into an understanding of the love of the Giver of all these gifts?*

The statement is frequently made that men and women wholly mentally absorbed and physically occupied in some great undertaking—inventors, scientists, astronomers and those engaged in other vocations requiring intense concentration—are able to live in continence with no ill effects.

Such a statement is based on a truthful fact, and on this fact are based the instructions for the healthy unmarried. These people intensely engaged in some specific work, concentrate their entire mental capacity on the object in view; follow in thought and desire the particular idea waking and sleeping; hence all power, forces and energies are drawn to a focal point, and used in the furtherance of the one object in life.

To such persons, continence is possible without harmful after effects. Consciously or unconsciously, they apply one of Nature's greatest laws—that of *transmutation*. The vital forces generated by the creative system are marshalled to the brain and absorbed through mental activity. Very few men in a generation are able to do this.

Many of the ablest physicians of the past and present declare that men of this type border on insanity; in fact, that genius *is* a form of insanity. The mind concentrated, day in and day out, on one thing, is unbalanced, one-sided, and abnormal in respect to other things; while the unexercised capability of sex gradually decreases, and if continence continues, is finally destroyed; the *fountain of youth is dried up, is lost forever.*

Considering everything, are we not justified in claiming that no one, great or small, can practice continence without injury to themselves and others? Even in the case of genius, if the foundation of the love nature is destroyed, is he not that much the poorer? Has he not wronged humanity, as well as himself, in placing himself where it is impossible for him to love, and feel, with the rest of the race?

Are we not safe in venturing the remark that the genius could still have given the world the benefit of his mighty intellect, and yet have kept the roots of his love nature alive and flourishing? The love embrace is not always essential to such a nature to prevent the death of the desire. There are many temperaments that store the vital fluid slowly; nature does not demand the same activity of all men.

The problems of domesticity and "the vice of nations" cannot be overlooked. When the wife believes in and practices continence, what is the husband to do? Because the woman chooses to consistently follow what he *honestly* FEELS is the *Path of Death,* is it good and sufficient to force him to live in a manner he is convinced will bring about his impotence and incompetence?

Many husbands, men of honor and decency, are refused "their natural right"; because of emotional coldness, religious scruples, or other unsound reasons. Alas, some of these men have denied themselves until nature could bear the pressure no longer.

Which is worse, disease, insanity, or the seeking of a mistress? The latter method is at least the normal, natural way out of the dilemma, even though not entirely endorsed by God or the moral law.

Cases? Their number is legion! Who is to blame? Who shall judge such men guilty of adultery? *What is adultery?* When is unlegalized indulgence adultery? Why did God give men desire, passion, love, all the possibilities of growth and happiness and then shut the door to all fulfillment? He *never did.* He did not bestow upon men all the blessings of temperament and then say: *"Thou shalt not."*

If the embrace of the woman who is his wife is denied him, *other than because of illness or an unpreventable cause,* if his health, saneness, ability, and happiness depend upon what the wife refuses, who shall say that morality demands that he, the husband, makes the renunciation? What is the answer?

This is dangerous ground, even for discussion. It borders on free love, *a doctrine we are utterly opposed to with all the force of our being.* Free love, promiscuity and license has nothing to do with the Laws of God and the right use of the creative function; *absolutely nothing.* But every phase of the problem—use, non-use, and abuse—all must be faced squarely and a solution found.

We are not giving consideration to the moral leper who is unsatisfied with the wife who gives him the full benefit of her love, yet continually seeks out other women to satisfy his lust. We have in mind only the man of honor, not the libertine; the man who learns through experience that normal sex indulgence is necessary for the preservation of his health and well-being, not the debauchee whose creed is license.

What is to be done? *There exists a remedy for every ill; a cure for every evil.* The solution of this difficulty should be effected without delay; not only for the sake of the suffering, unhappy men and women, but for the sake of the children being born of such unions and denied the opportunity to develop normally.

What is the remedy? Are legislative enactments of actual help? Suppose the evidence is conclusive that either husband or wife fails, *by choice,* not as the result of ill-health or other natural cause, to fulfill their conjugal duty for a given length of time, and a divorce were granted on this basis, would this solve the problem? Suppose there were a family, children requiring the care of a father and mother? Would a Solomon have the answer?

To recapitulate: The correct exercise of sex is of supreme importance, not alone to the individual man and woman, but even more so to the world at large. If a man attempts to live, or is compelled to live, the continent life for any length of time, the pool of creative energy becomes stagnant; a poison to his entire system; not only affecting both his health, and his mentality, but also his future progeny, if any. This, in turn, affects the economy of the world.

Non-use of the creative energy, like non-use of any other power, energy or potentiality, creates inertia and stagnation— and these conditions, in the human organism, invite disease, decay and death. This is a direct violation of the laws of God who created ALL THINGS FOR USE.

CONTINENCE

The Living Dance of "Death"

ONTINENCE and Libertinism, though diametrically opposite in practice, have this one outstanding point in common: they both aim straight at the very foundations of life. Equally baneful in their ultimate effect on the human organism, they are but dual aspects of the "Dance of Death." We are not, at the moment, engaged in a philosophical dissertation on the means of REgeneration, although some reference to the problem seems to be in order at this point.

While all of life begins with generation, it should end with REgeneration or Immortalization, *i.e.* MORTALITY TAKING ON IMMORTALITY. REgeneration or Immortalization proceed hand in hand with Race REgeneration and, together, constitute the Divine Mystery of Sex. The "seed" known and accepted as the *means* of generation, is likewise the medium of REgeneration.

This duality of the "seed" was well understood by the ancient Initiate Priests or *true* Holy men. Moses, one of the most notable of these, taught the Israelites that if they "cast the 'seed' to Moloch," by any practice, it would become a "serpent" or destroyer of the Soul itself; bringing disease and death upon whoever would be guilty of the practice, while those who "raised up the serpent" as exemplified by himself, "upon the Cross" would have greater life and be "saved."

Considered in terms of the ultimate, the effect upon man,

both as concerns his body and Soul, or what the church generally terms "the spirit," it matters little whether this "seed" is cast upon the ground as a result of the unfinished marital embrace, the practice of various forms of solitary vice—self-pollution— or unjustified continence. In either case, the penalty is the same.

It may logically be questioned whether the "seed" is not also lost in the marital rite when pregnancy does not follow. *Emphatically not in the normal embrace.* Whether pregnancy *does or does not result,* there is an exchange of the vital forces of life between the twain.

The semen is the agent or carrier of these vital, positive, electric, creative forces to woman; while she, in, and by, the *lochia,* releases to man the vital magnetic forces. The exchange of these vital life forces between man and woman, are essential to health, normalcy of mind and balance.

Countless wives continually discourage husbands from completing the marital rite, due to fear of pregnancy. These women soon become haggard in appearance and old long before their time; nervous wrecks after a few years of married life.

The repeated interruption of the rite and the resulting lack of mutual exchange results first in congestion, then irritation and, finally, in an increased desire for *Coitus,* a vicious circle of destruction to health and well-being.

The husband suffers similarily; first a congestion, then irritation; finally seeking relief elsewhere than in the home; or shunning that, turns to excessive drinking or other debauchery for relief.

The constant declaration of those who lack knowledge of the subject is that continence is the law of life; that *Coitus* engaged in for reasons other than generation results in the death of an infinite number of living cells and is a waste. The argument is specious.

Even if pregnancy results through the practice of the marital rite, it does so only about once in a hundred times, and even then BUT ONE spermatozoon impregnates and fecundates the ovum; the rest of the more than a million spermatozoons released offer their lives on the altar of service; giving their lives and collective vitality to the one "seed" fortunate enough to impregnate the ovum.

Many who inculcate the doctrine of continence base their delusive reasoning on Biblical precepts, making them all the more insidious and readily acceptable by those who are seeking a way and means to avoid their full duty. Before us is a printed sheet promoting this class of destructive teaching called "Livable Christianity" and we quote:

"It is indulgence in the sensations of the flesh that disorganizes the finer forces of the consciousness. Fleshly desires, expressed or yearning to be expressed, kill out the connection with the spiritual nature within, and turns the body, which should show forth the loveliness of God-mind, into a carnal house of disease and discord. All attempts to satisfy one's desires, whatever be their nature, through outside alliance gives the lie to the truth that man is complete in himself, satisfied from God, and ultimately leads to dissatisfaction, woe and death."

The theory of continence built on such reasoning, appears to be sound and consistent with God's law, but a little reasoning brings to light the *utter falsity* of the statements. Nowhere in sacred Scriptures are the sensations of the flesh forbidden. Sinning, that is, misuse alone, is forbidden. Moreover, if any human being actually tried to destroy sensation, i.e., feeling, he would be destroying life, because life itself is based on sensation or feeling.

The author evidently never heard the Biblical command: "Render unto Caesar that which belongs to Caesar (to the flesh that which belongs to the flesh) and unto God that which belongs to God (to the spirit that which belongs to the spirit)." This is the absolute law of duality without which nothing could exist. It also explains that everything is made for use—right use—that only misuse or wrong use is forbidden.

Furthermore, man is *not* complete in himself—"Man does not live by himself alone,"—until after "mortality has put on Immortality," hence but few on earth today *are* complete in themselves and we are not dealing with these few here.

With teachings such as these broadcast to a gullible people seeking a "way out" of responsibility, can we wonder that immorality is increasing beyond all reason? Such teachings as these and "I Amism," are not livable Christianity.

They are the "Dance of death," and are promulgated by those who have been abnormally born; or who have lived in degrading environments; or who perhaps were disappointed in love, and became "soured" on the natural way of living. Also to be considered here are those who, because of past practices, are no longer competent, hence no longer MEN and WOMEN; all seeking an excuse to justify themselves and their past, if not their present, shortcomings.

It is our contention that anyone who attempts to follow instructions such as these will not sip the "drink of life," but drain the dregs of degradation. No vitally living human being without a legitimate reason is able to dam up the fountain of life and keep the waters "fresh." It is physically, mentally and spiritually impossible. We say "legitimate reason," and mean just that. If there is a sound and sane reason for the necessity of so doing, then psychological factors enter into the problem and these then govern, modifying the results.

The teachings of youth may influence all of life for better or worse. We have in mind the experience of a maiden lady into whose mind had been instilled the undesirability of sex expression in woman and the shame of experiencing an orgasm. This lady had lived an absolutely virtuous life, when, at the age of thirty-eight, she fell in love and was married to a man in full possession of his *manhood*.

Through endearments she was made conscious of the falsity of her earlier instructions and the awakening of a desire to reciprocate affection to the full. What was her horror to find that, try as she would, she could not be brought to the normal climax and the keen relaxation that always follows. Her very Soul seemed to cry out to her: "Thus far and no farther canst thou go." Attempt after attempt was made to unlock the floodgate of love and obtain relief and ease, but without success. Gradually, the nervous system became acutely affected, and the lady, broken in courage, health and spirit, at last sought relief from one who understood.

The errors of the past teachings were pointed out to her and when she fully understood her errors, a deep psychological change took place in her inner self. Freedom took the place of the bondage to erroneous ideas. Gradually, she became normal in thought and feeling and began to regain her health and the enjoyment to which her wedded love entitled her.

We have outlined some of the more extreme results of the continent life as we have found them in our years of service.

There are many lesser evils which ought to be of sufficient warning to reasonable, rational, human beings.

The first indication of trouble may be nervousness in any one of its various forms, and without apparent cause. Then follow other disturbing symptoms in rapid succession; possibly an irritability making the person a most undesirable companion; gloomy, "touchy," disposed to look on the dark side of everything. More advanced symptoms include loss of appetite and malnutrition; incapacity to concentrate; lack of decision and stick-to-it-ness; desire for constant change; nervous headaches due to a deranged nervous system; inability to digest even simple food; constipation and toxo-absorption; ending in neurasthenia, just a step removed from mental incapacity.

The *debauchee's* life precipitates about the same general weaknesses. The wasting of the life forces depletes them faster than man can accumulate them. The mixture of different rates of vibration; various currents of magnetic forces coming from many women, will destroy the strongest man, demagnetizing him, and shattering his life forces.

Continence is a dragon with an hundred heads; each with a sting of death.

In many instances the devotee, if a male, experiences just the opposite of the torrefaction—drying up—of the vivifying forces. There may be an unnatural accumulation. This, together with a lesion of the generative organism, induces continuous nocturnal emissions; leading to pronounced spermatorrhea and loss of manhood, with consequent depletion of the entire nervous system. No need to write of the wrecks brought about through this process of degeneration, for nearly everyone is personally familiar with such cases and their deplorable effects.

One of the most degrading and hideous habits, especially in

the male, following in the wake of continence is masturbation and for two reasons: it has a profound psychological effect on the mind which brings on a sense of degradation; it is self-pollution and drains the system of *vital* fluids, gradually reducing virility. It is the death-dealing sin of "Casting the seed upon the ground."

Moreover, the tendency of the continent man or woman to perversion is much greater than imagined; the temptation to find satisfaction in one manner or another, other than the natural, is so insiduous that the victim succumbs to it before he or she is actually aware of it.

We cannot find an argument in favor of the destructive practice of continence. Admittedly, there are periods in the lives of most men when it is both right and expedient to abstain from the sexual embrace; as when the wife is ill, or during the absence of either one or the other from the home; but this is merely abstinence, not continence; *and the mind does not dwell on the enforced denial; rather looks cheerfully forward to the resumption of the natural love tie.*

What of the effects of continence on the happiness of the home? *Those harmoniously mated best bear the strain and stress of married life who practice the marriage rite naturally and normally.* Normally here implies that the couple are agreed, not only in regard to time, but likewise in desire. In some instances this may be but once a week, or once in two weeks; in the majority of cases it has reference to two or three embraces regularly every week during the years of youth, except during the period of the wife's unholiness.

A husband should indicate his desire by additional caresses and affection; and only when he has succeeded in arousing the wife's similar desires may the rite be performed. No man should touch a woman until she has indicated *willing* compliance. Under these conditions health, peace, and happiness are the natural accompaniments of the embrace. If a man brutally ignores a woman's feelings and forces his attentions upon her, he commits a crime no less than married prostitution, ignoble license.

The confession of every human being, could it be secured, would undoubtedly be this: In every case, without one exception, where man and woman are agreed in time and desire, they have parted more in love and harmony with each other after the performance of the rite, than before.

Countless men and women can tell of the woes and miseries of being mismated. The husband, lacking in manly strength, leaving the wife unsatisfied; or the wife, fearing pregnancy, refusing embrace, or half-heartedly submitting, and so on *ad infinitum.* In most instances, the ultimate result is unhappiness, illness, mutual distrust, a gradual cooling of the affections; the husband finally seeking a mistress; the wife a lover, or divorce.

Teachers of continence may assert that the diseases and effects here attributed to continence are as easily applied to those indulging in the marriage rite. We have already admitted all this. The penalty for abuse of sex, in or out of wedlock, is equally as severe as for the practice of unnecessary continence.

In other respects the proof may be declared absolute. For example: The long sex life of the man who practices the marriage rite normally; while the continent man cannot claim longevity of sex. Admittedly, if the latter is consistent, he does not seek continued virility. The argument favors the potency of sex; *the man being considered as youthful, or in his prime only so long as he retains his virility.* Thereafter, he is an "old man."

One point remains undisputed. Neither man nor woman has any right to practice the marriage rite without love as the *impetus*. If the act is performed under any other thought, desire, or incentive, it is a violation; and a marriage ceremony, irrespective of who may have performed it, cannot set aside the great fiat flung into space by God.

If there is no real affection between husband and wife, if they do not love each other, and the husband *demands* conjugal "rights" and she complies, they are both guilty of a form of prostitution. The woman will not, *cannot,* release the magnetic forces and the man is incapable of infusing the vital forces. The climax may occur; there will be a sort of physical satisfaction, but neither receives the psychic, or spiritualized essence which should always be the aim of cohabitation; *the vital essential to health, strength, peace and happiness to both.*

Writers and instructors have emphasized the act in itself, or the elimination of it altogether, missing the important point just enunciated, which *must* be the underlying fundamental insisted upon in Race Regeneration. Until this is fully understood and practiced, misery and weakness will continue to be the "benefit" of the marriage rite.

Much comment has been voiced upon the love starvation of the race. *Love is, and always has been.* It is as natural and as necessary to every human being as food. The advocates of continence would have us believe that we may love without passion. *That is utterly impossible.* The moment a man dearly and sincerely loves a woman, one of the expressions of that emotion is possession for him; with her it is to *be* possessed.

God created man in His own image; that is, He conferred

upon man wisdom and love, the attributes of Himself. The fact that man manifests in the material while God manifests in the spiritual, is nowise a contradiction. Men are co-workers with Jehovah, the Creator, and the creative, generative organism, together with the *inherent desire to function thereby,* substantiates this assertion.

Had it been ordained that men and women should live separately as sex weaklings, God never would have implanted in man so generously the incentive to creative expression; nor would He have instilled in man the urge for more or less frequent companionship, ending in embrace with the beloved. Had He intended the indulgence to occur once a year, or once in two years, then only for the purpose of reproduction, He would have changed human emotions and desires to conform with such a law.

Were it true that man is capable of loving without passion, then the opposite would be equally true; men then could and should perform the creative act without the incentive of love. Such a thought is revolting; the consequences even more so; it is beastly, unhuman, degrading.

Love lies at the basis of passion; and in its correct understanding, *passion is the basis of love.* The potentiality in man to love, or hate, or achieve, is in direct ratio to the virility of his creative potency. The weakly sexed, cannot surely love. Therefore:

The man living the continent life is incapable of expressing love in its highest aspect.

BABYLONIANISM

A Straight Road to Self-Degradation and Damnation

ERY few writers in the past have had the courage to speak plainly and openly of depravities which have caused the destruction of nations and which may be classified under the general term Babylonianism.

This entire subject, disgusting as it admittedly is, can no longer be avoided, because of the publication of several books by a physician. These books have had a wide circulation, teaching a practice so destructive that it quickly degrades and destroys body and Soul.

It is essential to quote *verbatim* from one of these books that we may comment on the inculcations of conjugal frauds, though we will eliminate abhorrent words and phrases as much as possible and substitute words less repulsive to sensitive minds.

"The hand of the opposite sex will produce effects on the genitals of the other which will not be produced in any other way. Thus a man may hold his *glans* in his own hand for a given length of time, longer or shorter, and no results will be effected, no secretions of the prostatic fluid will at once take place. This is true whether the *glans* be erect or detumescent (relaxed).

"If the wife will hold her husband's limp glans in her hand for but a few minutes, even though the organ remains limp, the flow of the prostatic fluid will take place. The same is true with regard to the husband's putting his hand on his wife's vulva. Should she hold her hand there, no pre-coital fluid would be secreted. With her husband's hand there, the flow would at once begin.

"This is a remarkable physical and psychological phenomenon, and it is one especially worthy of note. It is this fact that makes *mutual* masturbation far superior to auto-erotism.[1] A husband can thus satisfy a wife with his fingers, or a wife her husband with her hand, far better than either could bring herself or himself to the climax alone. This point is of great importance in considering many of the sex acts of husband and wife.

"As a rule, let the husband and wife do whatever their desire prompts or suggests, and just as they feel they desire. Only this, let all be in moderation. Carry nothing to excess!"

Neither Sodom, Gomorrah, or Babylon were guilty of a practice more damnable and destructive than this. Because of its apparent innocence it quickly seduces its victims and degrades them beyond rehabilitation before they are aware that the mutual fraud is destroying body and Soul. Like solitary vice, the practice readily becomes a habit, and once established is far more difficult to overcome than ordinary harlotry.

The great sin is not as much in the mutual practice itself, as in the *Soul searing* deed of *"giving the seed unto Moloch."* We have already treated at length the results of this act, illustrating it by the experience of the Israelites when on their way to the Promised Land; and it would seem that we, in what

---

[1]The author gives this practice its proper name. It is mutual pollution of the most degrading type and those who really love each other will not be guilty of such a practice. It is degrading to an unnamable degree and following this rite, those who practice it will not be able to look each other in the eyes. No language contains words sufficiently strong to condemn it properly.

should be a sane and enlightened age, are to *react the carnage of lust of which the ancient people were guilty, destroying body and Soul.*

Time and again we have emphasized the *absolutely irrevocable law* that the marriage rite may be indulged only for three purposes: Procreation, Recreation and REgeneration. It is Divinely forbidden for man and woman to seek gratification for *self-satisfaction and pleasure alone.* There must always be a deeper incentive as already pointed out; such as the mutual exchange of the magnetic-electric forces between those engaged in the rite, or for self-elevation and spiritualization.

The *demonic* practice of exterior sex satisfaction advocated by this author and others is solely for carnal purposes, therefore degrading and destructive to morality and spirituality. It is sense-gratification; condemned by God and *every* Creative Law. It quickly destroys moral sensibility, so that men and women guilty of this practice quickly degrade themselves below the animal plane; becoming shameless, unmoral creatures, lacking understanding of the true meaning of love and all that is related to it.

God in his primary creation acted wisely when he constituted man so that any abuse of the creative function would be detrimental to both mind and Soul. Any waste of the seminal fluid, whether by conjugal fraud or the advocated type of mutual masturbation, results in loss of brain and nerve force, ultimately resulting in some form of neurosis, and finally in the destruction of the Soul itself; eliminating even the *possibility* of life after death.

In truth, it is far easier for the legendary camel to pass through the eye of a needle, *than for two creatures in the human form, who mutually abuse and thereby degrade each other, to enter the kingdom known as heaven.*

Admittedly, the wife's fondling of the genital organs of the husband may induce the prostatic fluids to flow, and likewise will the husband's touch release the pre-coital flow in the woman, and for this reason it is to be avoided at all times, except possibly under certain circumstances as a *preliminary* to the marital rite in those of a more or less frigid nature.

Even so, great care should be exercised not to continue the fondling for too long a time, lest it results in weakening the strength of one or the other of the participants. *This practice is permissable only as a preparation for the normal marital embrace.*

We emphatically contradict that release of the prostatic fluid in the male, and the pre-coital lochia in the female, under such excitation is a remarkable physical phenomenon. Pyschological it undoubtedly is, but not in the least mysterious.

The youth when sexually anhungered can, by the mere play of his imagination, see himself in relation with some fancied companion, and thereby induce the prostatic flow. Many girls and women have confessed to us being able to do likewise. It is therefore nothing more or less than the arousing of the physical creative desires by awakening the imaginative faculty to a degree necessary to produce the flow and consequent relaxation; *it is self fraud.* To continue our quotation:

"Let it be said further, that auto-erotism, self-spending, may be practiced by both men and women, to their healthful benefit,[2] when sexual excitement cannot be secured in any other way. It is only when carried to excess that such action is in any way harmful. The only danger is that the individual being alone and having all the means for self-gratification in his or her own hands, so to speak, it is quite possible to indulge in the action too freely, which, of course, leads to bad results. *But the act itself is not bad.* On the contrary, when kept within bounds, it is healthful and wholesome."[2]

Clearly our learned author is illogical. Previously he made the statement that *mutual* masturbation was more desirable and pleasurable than solitary vice; now he tells us that the individual, having all the means at hand, may over-indulge. If it is true that mutually *committing the crime*—we say "committing the crime" advisedly—gives greater pleasure than the solitary act, and if self-spending—more correctly termed "self-pollution"—is vice-forming, then how much more so is the intensely pleasure-giving, though degrading, double criminal act?

Auto-erotism, so termed because even the habitues to it are ashamed to apply its rightly designated name—masturbation or self-pollution—is a crime against the self and God. Every "fall" results from the "casting upon the ground" of millions of "seed," which would either help in the creation of a new being if properly consigned; in the *re*creation of the self-being if *transmuted;* or in the *re*juvenation of the twain taking part in the exchange in the lawful manner.

Self-pollution is a crime because it sets at variance *every creative law.* All who are guilty of the pernicious practice are thereafter ashamed to look themselves squarely in the eyes by the aid of a mirror; as well as squarely face their fellow creatures.

---

[2]We make the positive statement that this is *never* true. Health, that is, normalcy, which means naturalness, can never be the result of *un*-naturalness, or of any act which destroys the very essence of life, the vital forces necessary for the maintenance or restoration of health. If the claim were correct, then all our natural laws would be in error. An act is either right or it is wrong; a wrong act cannot be productive of a righteous result.

It is only when continued for a length of time sufficient to break down the moral stamina, indicating likewise a loss of brain and Soul force, that the practitioner of solitary vice or mutual masturbation, becomes *blase* enough to face his own emaciated self and the world at large, without pangs of conscience.

The practice is demoralizing even if indulged infrequently, because a certain amount of vital force is wasted without the possibility of recovery. It is giving something and receiving nothing, therefore robbery of the self, hence is self-defrauding. The more frequently practiced, the nearer man, or the woman, draws to the brink of moral degradation and physical imbecility. The act in itself is evil; it is debasing; unfitting *every* man who is guilty, to meet face to face any pure woman; not mentioning meeting the Giver of Life.

"There are many unmarried women, maiden ladies, and especially widows, who would greatly improve their health if they practiced some form of auto-erotism occasionally."

We personally place ourselves on record as voicing the sentiment, that if the sexual desire of any woman, whether maiden lady or widow, becomes so insistent that relief is actually necessary, then it would be *far* better for them, body and Soul, and the world at large, to follow the old religious practice of the maidens of India—veil their faces and sit before the temple—accepting the offer of the first man that passes.

Thus would the relief sought be obtained; seed would not be cast upon the ground; and they would receive in exchange an amount of vital magnetic force equal to that expended by their creative organism.

We do *not* advocate such method of seeking relief from the thraldom of passion, but we do maintain that if relief *must* be obtained, this would be a thousand-fold preferable to the seed-wasting, disease-inducing, lust-engendering practice of self-pollution as advocated.

"As a matter of fact, all boys masturbate, and many girls also[3]. Some authors claim that more than half of the women engaged in some form of auto-erotism, at some time in their lives, and the estimate is probably too low rather than too high. But unless they carry the act to excess, they are guilty of no wrong[4]. Not infrequently, they may make the act a means of great good to themselves. The sex organs are alive! They constantly secrete fluids that need to be excreted, as all other organs of the body do. They ought to be relieved, as their nature requires they should be."[5]

It is utterly false that all boys are guilty of self-pollution. Admittedly the majority are, ignorantly so, but this does not permit any man to teach that it is right to practice self-abuse.

Likewise it is true that many girls are victims of the habit, and with what results? We have known of women who indulged in the destructive practice before they were married, and after marriage preferred it to the natural creative embrace;

---

[3]Even if this were true, the practice is not justified by any moral, health or spiritual law. Our author does not state how many have become degenerates, physical or mental weaklings as a result of the practice.

[4] If plural masturbation and the consequent pollution is not wrong, then there is no sex sin and boys and girls, as well as men and women, may commit all the abnormal practices they wish with no penalty attached.

Moreover, the Bible and all its teachings may be discarded. The many writers who dwelt on the evils in various forms of degradation as the result of "casting the seed upon the ground," must be in error. It is equally certain that all writers opposing this view are not to be accepted as teaching Divine Law to mankind.

[5]This statement is true in fact, but the implications are false. There should be relief, but this must be by means of *right use*, not by ABUSE; by the application of natural laws; a correct and non-irritating, non-stimulating diet, exercise, transmutation of the forces, reabsorption into the blood stream and other methods both simple and effective. Nature will co-operate with those who will co-operate with nature.

allowing their husbands to caress and fondle them until their desires were fully aroused, then turning the cold shoulder to them; defrauding both themselves and their husbands by a recurrence to the old degrading habit. Can any one imagine anything more abominable than this? Yet this is what perverters of human virtues inculcate.

True, the sexual organism is an active entity; constantly secreting fluids that are life-giving; it being essential to health and well-being to keep these vital forces in circulation—this offers no excuse for abuse or the waste of the vital life forces—it is merely an indication that they should be naturally utilized; the method being either through a reabsorption into the circulation and a transmutation into physical, mental and Soul forces; or an exchange between the male and female.

God created the two, male and female created He them; He comprehended that neither one nor the other could possibly be sufficient unto the self, consequently He gave them the means to mate. Auto-erotism is a crime greater than murder or patricide, because the practice destroys the *self;* redemption then becomes impossible. We quote again:

"Sometimes, during the five days of menstruation, during which time the union of the organs is deemed not best, the wife can thus help her lover with her hand, to his delight and benefit."

We would inquire, what of the woman during this period? If he suffers, how much greater must be the longing on her part as she fondles him, but is herself denied, and what must be her reactions?

Undeniably there are men so strong in their virility that they keenly feel the deprivation of exercise during these few days,

but if they are mentally developed in proportion to their manhood, and not merely male animals, they gladly suffer tempor-
arily because the possibilities for love become so much greater
and more intensified during the short period of waiting. As
a matter of fact, we find that the true man looks forward to
these temporary rests in the knowledge that there will be
greater satisfaction to both after the interval of waiting.

If any man is so weak mentally and morally as to be unable
to control his desires during the period of her cleansing, that he
must be guilty of self-pollution, then it would be far better for
him to avoid all association with the woman by sleeping in a
separate bed, or that failing, do just as the animals in the field—
disgustingly cohabiting during the lunar season, and be stamped
with the mark of Cain. This would actually not be as grievous
a sin as the one-sided auto-erotism.

Greece, once the most enlightened and cultured nation on
the face of the earth, fell into decadence through the Cult of
Sappho. Sappho, the poetess, taught her own peculiar practice of
mutual masturbation and auto-erotism, and gradually these debaucheries became so universal that parents who foresaw the
end of the race because of it, paid their maids to become the
mothers of their sons' children; all to no avail, the prostitution
of the creative ability had become so extended that the nation
was doomed, possibly never to become great again.

Babylonia, one of the centers of the richest, proudest and
most cultured races then on earth, met its doom through similar
practices, the degradation finally becoming so great that the
"Lord saw fit to bring destruction upon Babylon." Noted Di-
vines preach on the destruction of Babylon and of the wicked-
ness of its people, but are extremely reticent in mentioning
what these sins really were, either ignorant or unmindful of

the fact that right here in America cults that inculcate and practice these identical sins are daily becoming more numerous.

Perhaps the greater responsibility rests upon the church (this includes all denominations) for either ignoring this most vital subject, or teaching that sex itself is evil; a sin, and that as all men are born by means of it, ALL MEN ARE BORN IN SIN. It is high time they reversed themselves and taught the truth:

> Sex is not an evil; something to hide, or of which to be ashamed, but a grandly sublime and glorious divine gift from the Creator to His creation, making them co-creators with Him. It is a means to health, strength, success and happiness; to the REjuvenation of the self-being and final Immortalization; "Mortality putting on Immortality." Through the means of sex man becomes, finally, like the gods, "knowing good from evil." At the same time, it teaches all mankind the penalty for abusing or degrading the creative function.

Sodom and Gomorrah were "destroyed by the Lord," *i.e.,* BURNED THEMSELVES UP, by their own sexual excesses and abuses. Men became the lovers of their own sex; women preferred women; other destructive and degrading practices were legion. All of these are now openly advocated in America.

Greece, Egypt, Sodom and Gomorrah, Babylonia and Rome all trace the beginning of their decadence to ease and the result of debasing practices which had their inception in the inculcation and practice of demonical rites, such as advocated by our Dr. L. and others seeking the maximum of pleasure with the minimum of responsibility.

Multitudes, especially men and women who desire the pleasure of sexual excitement, but shun the responsibility of parentage, are easily led to believe there is no harm in such practices.

Gradually and insidiously it masters them. To one *mode of procedure* away from the natural, is added another until, at last, none satisfy and they are first, the victims, then the perpetrators, and inculcators, of the most hideous vices malicious minds can conceive.

Is America, the proud nation over which the Eagle takes its flight, to have a list of thousands of ultra-cultured people guilty of all the sex abuses catalogable, as had England during the world war?

Is America to begin the downward path toward doom, similar to that trod by Greece, Rome and other past great nations? From the present trend, judging by the contents of books and magazines dealing with sex life and sex practices, we are doomed to meet a similar fate.

CONJUGAL FRAUD

The Destroyer of Marital Happiness

PPARENTLY, the author so frequently quoted in the preceding chapter, is not merely the high priest of the *cultus auto-eroticus;* of single and mutual pollution; but equally so of the universal wrecker of marital happiness, generally known as conjugal fraud.

Under the caption *Coitus Reservatus,* also called *Coitus Interruptus,* meaning the commencement of the marriage rite in harmony with nature's dictates, proceeding almost to the climax, then discontinuing for the time being, he tells us:

"It *should* be the constant aim and endeavor of both parties to continually lift all sex affairs above the plane of animality, mere physical gratification, into the realm of mental and spiritual delight."[6]

"To this end, let it be said at once that such a condition can be reached, in the greatest degree, by the practice of what is known, in scientific terms, as *coitus reservatus,* which, translated, means going only *part* of the way in the act, and not carrying it to its climax, the organism *(orgasm).* Described in terms with which the reader is now familiar, it means, carrying the act only through the first and second stages, the "courting

---

[6] This statement has our whole-hearted approval. The marital relationship *should* most certainly be lifted *above* the animal plane and the practice he teaches does this because no living animal would be guilty of such practices; but that *Coitus Reservatus,* a cheating and defrauding of one another can possibly be considered as a spiritual practice, even though it may be a *carnal* (below human) delight, is beyond the conception of the normal mind.

stage," in common parlance, *teasing,* the union of the organs (to near climax) and stopping there!"

"Going a bit into details, this act of *reservatus* really unites the first two parts of the act into a common whole, making it simply one continuous piece of "courting," merely that, and nothing more.

"To engage in this form of coitus, not nearly the effort should be made to arouse the sexual passions of either of the parties, as has already been described as fitting for complete coitus. The organism (orgasm) is not desideratum in this case, but it is just a delightful expression of mutual love.

"It is a sort of prolonged and all embracing kiss, in which the sex organs are included as well as the lips. They kiss each other as the lips kiss each other. It is "courting," par excellence, without the hampering of clothes or conventionality of any kind."

Here we have a perfect example of the modern method of procedure in conjugal fraud, one of the most damnable practices now cursing the marriage relationship, totally contrary to every law of nature and God, if we do not consider the Bible a book of lies in both the human and subhuman realms. Not one word can be said in its favor.

The practice of mutual masturbation previously considered, destroys the parties participating by draining them gradually of their virile force without replacing it through exchange.

This defrauding burns up the body and Soul, because *the creative forces are centered for the purpose of both relief and exchange, only to be* denied expression at the last moment, resulting in congestions, followed by irritations and many other ailments.

The author does not actually believe his own inculcations.

In speaking of the male weakling, who has not sufficient manly strength to satisfy the longings of his mate, he writes:

"After a man has passed the orgasm, it is, in most cases, impossible for him to continue the act, right then and there, and bring the woman to the climax, if she has not yet arrived, from the fact that, with the expulsion of the semen, usually detumescence of the glans at once takes place, and the organ is incapable of exciting the woman when in this condition.[7]

"If the husband *is ahead* first, there is no possibility of the wife's reaching the climax at that embrace. *This leaves her unsatisfied, all her sex organs congested, and the whole situation is unsatisfactory in the extreme.*"

We fully concur in the last sentence as it expresses exact facts. We have italicized them to call the reader's special attention to the truths voiced; thus clearly indicating how inconsistent is the average writer on these subjects, and how illogical his conclusions.

In instances of indulgence in the sexual embrace, where the strength of the husband is insufficient for the satisfaction of his wife, forcing him to discontinue the marriage rite before she reaches the climax, he at least bathes her creative organism with the seminal fluid; doing much toward reducing the inflammation and irritation resulting from unsatisfied desire.

In conjugal fraud, termed *reservatus,* not even this occurs. The congested, inflamed organism is forced to attempt gradually to "throw back" into circulation the blood *and* the fluids which were held ready for expulsion and exchange at the crisis; and has to contend with the after-irritation without the soothing serums to relieve the intensity of it.

---

[7] If, or when, this is true, it is due either to ignorance or weakness. Proper instructions or treatment will quickly rectify the error.

If, as the author admits, *and which we maintain is true,* the unsatisfied desire of the wife and consequent congestion has serious results on her health, how much greater, think you, is the continuous congesting and resulting irritation following the *repeated* conjugal fraud *(reservatus)* suggested; lacking the cooling and healing effects of being bathed by the seminal fluid?

We have personally listened to the confessions and treated an uncounted number of women suffering from the effects of love-hunger as the result of weakness in the husbands. These wives were to be pitied, but could be helped by careful instructions.

In most instances they accepted the situation, being mindful of the "for better or for worse" of the marriage ceremony; respecting their husbands, believing them blameless.

At the same time, we have come in close relationship with an almost equal number of women whose husbands continually defraud them by *coitus reservatus;* most of these poor wives are beyond hope; having lost faith in nature, man and God.

They are "burned out," like hollow trees ravished by forest fires; the inner spirit crushed and shrunken; the Soul seared and distorted; sex itself having become the serpent creeping in the dust on its belly and, like it, cursed by God.

Even these can be saved if they are willing to obey, but most of them are no longer possessed of sufficient stamina to make the required effort toward self-redemption.

In the quotation to follow, the author foolishly believes he is offering credulous man the key to the Paradise of Love; whereas, as a fact, he is teaching the most direct route to *Prostatic ailments,* the most dreadful ravages from which man can suffer; frequently termed the "hell-fire" of middle to old age.

"This method is of special service during the 'unfree time.' If rightly used, it will not tend to increase the desire for 'spending,' but it will, on the contrary, allay and satisfy the sexual desires, most perfectly.

"If, while learning how, sometimes the inexperienced should 'get run away with,' and feel that it is better to go on and have the climax, all right. But, as time goes on, the practice of carrying the act only to the end of the second part, will grow, and in due time will be well established.[8] Those who have mastered this wholesome and loving[9] art will sometimes meet in this way a score of times during a month or so, without once coming to the climax."

It is illogical to claim that any organs as sensitive as those of the creative system can be brought to the highest state of expectancy, thoroughly enpassioned or tumescent, and then allowed to remain in that condition by refusal to give them relief, without serious damage to the human system.

Any one who has ever attempted this is aware that there is an intense feeling of uneasiness in the parts, inducing a physical and mental unrest which nothing but a normal and fully completed embrace can relieve.

Admittedly, if this practice is continued for any length of time and in the manner suggested, it will become established, but this is due to the weakening of the internal forces and the gradual loss of sensitiveness of the entire genital organism. It

---

[8] And, with it, almost every form of the so-called "male" and "female" trouble, paving the way for quacks and charlatans to reap rich harvests. Such an unwholesome situation is the basis for so many of the sorrows and miseries of married life.

[9] "Degrading and disgusting" practice would be a far more correct description. Whoever attempts to practice according to these instructions will soon find himself in the whirlpool of sex debasement and all that is subhuman.

is a process of "burning up," which results from the over-heating, without properly tempering, of any sensitive material substance.

Anyone posing as the inculcator of an art, or a method, should at least be consistent, but the author of this special system for the destruction of body and Soul, frequently contradicts himself, as note the following.

". . . ., if it sometimes happens that the husband should arrive at the climax before the wife does, and he could not bring her to an organism (orgasm) by excitation with the spent glans, it would be perfectly right for him to substitute his finger, and satisfy her in that way. Of course, this would not be as satisfying to her as it would have been could she have met him simultaneously, but it is far better than for her not to be entirely satisfied. *Many a woman suffers all night long with unsatisfied desire, her organs congested and tumescent, because she has been left unsatisfied by a husband who was spent before she was ready, and then left her!* Such cases might be entirely relieved, if the parties knew the truth, and were not too ignorant, or prejudiced, or ashamed, to do what should be done to make the best of a situation."

In one paragraph we are informed in detail how the embrace may be commenced, the act carried to almost the climax, and then discontinued, *without* increasing the desire for indulgence; on the contrary, allaying and satisfying the sexual appetite; in due time becoming established and a normal act.

Then he tells us of the suffering resulting to a woman when her desires remain unsatisfied[10], because of not being brought to the climax. These contradictions are met throughout the

---

[10] This description of such a woman's dissatisfaction and suffering is all too correct, and one of the chief causes of it is practices such as here advocated.

book, but do not render its several inculcations any the less dangerous because the ordinary reader, seeking a method offering the gratification of lust without obliging him to meet the responsibilities of his act, will not be apt to recognize these contradictions.

We heartily concur in the statement relative to the desirability of relieving the suffering of the woman resultant on her not being brought to the climax, but have never known of the necessity for semi-erotic practices on the part of the husband; one who is more or less of a weakling can be instructed in natural methods, making it possible for him to perform his manly conjugal duties with entire satisfaction.

The author's advice to the single is on a par with that offered the married, as note the following:

"If a bride and bridegroom knew enough to introduce each other to the delights of an organism (orgasm) by 'spending' each other by external excitation of the organs with their hands a few times before they united the organs at all, it would be to their lasting well-being. This is especially true for the bride. If her lover would take her in his arms, even with all her clothes on, as she sat on his lap, in their bridal chamber, alone, and stroked her vulva till she 'spent,' the chances are many to one that he would have introduced her to such joy that she would never forget it, all her life."

It is inconceivable that anyone living in the present century and possessing the education required to pass the strict examinations of a Medical College, could possibly be guilty of fostering upon an already bewildered people such unhuman, unnatural, degrading practices.

We are thinking of the father who, adoring his daughter and believing her innocence personified, with a feeling of assurance of having entrusted her into the care of a man who is certain to protect her from all that is evil and degrading!

What will be his reaction when he learns that he has permitted her to fall into the hands of a carnal brute who, leading her to believe that he is fondling her, carressing her and doing all in his power to prepare her for God's most holy exercise of the creative function, then proceeds to do to her one of the foulest of all deeds—masturbate her—an ugly word, but both truthful and descriptive; *what will he do?*

Whether such a Soul-shattering practice would bring her a "joy that she would never forget, all her life," depends entirely upon the morality and *finesse* of her character. If she is one begotten in a family where vulgarity is the rule of character, she may accept it as a natural incident, one to be expected; but if a girl-woman such as we have in mind, as hoping our daughter to be, she would slap the brute across the face, damn his Soul to perdition, and quickly seek relief in a Court of Justice.

The one thing in life that the mentally and physically normal young man looks forward to and a consummation he *never forgets,* is the entering of the *great unknown*—the first complete marriage embrace he enjoys with his bride. Were such a practice indulged, the rite following would be a farce, a parody on the Divine creative act.

"Indeed, if a bride to be, who was so innocent or ignorant of her sex possibilities that she had never experienced an organism (orgasm)—had never 'spent'—could be 'put wise' before her bridal night, if she could be instructed enough to lead her to engage in some form of auto-erotism, bringing herself to an *orgasm* with her own hand, just for the sake of the experience it would give her, and so that she would have some clear idea of what she really wanted, before she went into the arms of her lover—if she could do this, in the right mental attitude, it would be greatly to her well-being, a worthy and valuable addition to her stock of knowledge of herself and of the powers that are latent within her. Her alleged loss of innocence by such an act would be nothing compared with the wisdom she would gain by the experience."[11]

Established churches have inculcated the doctrine that the Serpent of Satan, once in the Garden of Eden, no longer exists; however, it is our firm opinion that if that particular serpent did die, then Satan (personified evil) has created one far superior to the original tempter; such instructions for the defilement of the innocent, emanating from it.

Apparently it is not sufficiently destructive to the race that many of our finest girls ignorantly and innocently fall victims to the habit of self-abuse, totally ignorant of the penalty to be paid later. We must now witness the spectacle of writers, accepted as authorities, teaching self-pollution to our maidens, deluding them into the belief the experience is necessarily wise and proper for obtaining sexual satisfaction.

Unquestionably such practices add both experience and wisdom to the sum total of the girl's possessions; but they likewise will be a constant reminder of degradation and self-pollution; a feeling of uncleanliness, and an incapacity to look into the eyes of the innocent youth without the ever-present thought of unworthiness.

Girls who fall victims to the habit, through the machinations of others equally guilty, can readily be forgiven. Theirs is not

---

[11]We may be in error, but it is our humble opinion that the demons of hell could not spawn forth an inculcation more disgusting and degrading than this.

a conscious guilt. The girl who deliberately degrades her most sacred treasure cannot be excused on any grounds.

We venture to say that if actual knowledge and experience is essential to the welfare of his daughter, the average father who is also a man in the true sense of the term, would far prefer to see his daughter in the arms of a clean man, even though he is not her husband, and the embrace righteously consummated, thus permitting them the continued freedom of being able to face their fellow-being and God without shame, than to have her guilty of this shameful practice, damned by God, causing the actor to hide the face with shame.

"The fact is, this whole matter of sexual excitation by means of the hand, or in any other way than the union of the organs, has received a black eye at the hands of would-be purists, which it in no way deserves. As already noted, the word masturbation has been fastened to such acts, and then, any and every form of it has been condemned far beyond what the facts warrant, till the minds of the rank and file are wholly misled in the premises! When one looks at the situation from the point of view which insists that all the sex functions should be under the control of the will, then light is thrown upon the entire subject. Seen in this way, any form of sex stimulation, or auto-erotism (auto-erotism meaning *self-satisfaction*) which is not carried to excess, is right and wholesome."

Answering this, we reiterate former statements:

First: Any attempt to relieve the creative organism from the vital, or seminal fluids, other than by the union of the male and female organisms, is self-abuse, self-pollution, and damned by God and all chaste minds.

Second: We are not purists, nor would-be purists. We consider everything God created as pure and holy, and its right use sanctioned by Him; but self-satisfaction in any form which necessitates the "casting of the seed upon the ground" is defrauding both to the self and God; therefore destructive to body and Soul alike; making of man eventually less than the lowest creature of the field.

Third: Let us thank God with our whole hearts that the rank and file are not yet inoculated with the practice of the "beasts" of Sodom, Gomorrah and Babylon; fortunate in remaining uninitiated in the "rites that damn the Soul." Let us hope they never will be.

Fourth: There is a vast difference between sex stimulation and self-gratification, by this writer termed "auto-erotism." "Sex stimulation" is properly applied to the method of arousing the self or one's partner to an intense desire for the embrace. This is natural, normal and desirable, and may be properly termed a display of affection and endearments. Auto-erotism is plain, every-day masturbation; a practice shunned by all normal clean-minded men and women.

Fifth: Self gratification is *never* wholesome; is *always* degrading and destructive. It should be avoided as the devil is said to flee Holy water.

Sixth: The creative law permits the excitation of the sexual organism only for the purpose of arousing the desire of the dormant party who is to become one of the participants in the divine drama. When this is accomplished, the union must take place; nor dare it be discontinued until both parties are at ease and at peace.

To do otherwise is to commit conjugal fraud and will certainly arouse the disgust of the one defrauded. The seminal fluid has for its purpose, aside from procreation, the "charging" of the entire person of the female; just as a current from a generator charges the cells of a battery; thus bringing peace and good-will to the entire being; while the magnetic forces in her *lochia* has an equally desirable benefit on the physical and mental being of the male.

Seventh: Either life or death are hidden in the marital embrace. It is the original "Tree of Life" that stands in the "midst" of the *Garden of Eden* for those who obey the Law and do not eat of the *forbidden* fruit. Self-satisfaction, eroticism, mutual eroticism and conjugal fraud of every form and every manner of embrace, not based on love and affection between those engaged in the marriage rite, are the forbidden fruit and are "plucked" from the "Tree of Death."

The conjugal act is a marriage, "marriage" meaning *union*, or Holy rite, when based on mutual desire, engaged in normally and naturally to final satisfaction. This results in love and affection between the two and from it are born the progeny of a greater world of the future on the one hand; Rejuvenation and REgeneration on the other, when the act has a spiritual basis, and in the ultimate, the REgeneration of the race.

THE SPIRITUAL SIGNIFICANCE OF SEX

OR almost one hundred years there has been established and laboring in America an organization[1] now world wide, having as one of its fundamental teachings the inculcation of a livable philosophy dealing with Race REgeneration and the spiritualization of sex.

This laudable activity has been, and continues to be, actively engaged in instructing its members in the positive tenet that God created man and woman in the first instance, in His own image, so that they, in turn, might imitate Him.

He at the same time conferred upon them the power and ability to employ this same creative potential in the REgeneration of their own self-being, thereby making certain that their "Mortality should take on Immortality" so that they might be enabled to begin living life eternal here and now.

The certainty of the possibility of Immortalizing the Soul of man (the term "Soul" being more correct than the word "spirit") by means of a moral life and the correct exercise of the procreative function, has been, and still is, almost universally denied. The general conception almost universally accepted, is that the sex function has no purpose beyond procreation of the species; plus the fact that the same function, if unwisely exercised, leads to degradation of the spiritual self.

This conception denies the laws of logic which teach us that all action is dual; that the pendulum of the clock must swing as far to the right as it does to the left in order that balance and activity (life) be maintained.

---

[1]See *Philosophy of Fire*, Philosophical Publishing Company, Quakertown, Pa.

If we admit the possibility that abuse of the creative function may bring about damnation, then it assuredly is sane to admit that its right and normal exercise has the potentiality of elevating the Soul above the carnal into the spiritual.

Creation on the human plane identifies the act whereby man brings into being a new body in preparation as the habitation for a Soul; REcreation or REgeneration is the method of transmuting the mortal into the Immortal; Biblically speaking "Mortality taking on Immortality."

Possibly, for a clearer distinction of terms, we might better say: REcreation is the process of REBIRTH spiritually; of so purifying the body that sickness and weakness will be eradicated. REgeneration is that greater work of bringing into active manifestation the mighty Soul, a counterpart of God—that part of man which is usually allowed to lie dormant; to return to the Father at death of the physical no more spiritualized than when it left Him to take up its habitation in the mortal frame.

To the majority of thinkers it appears incomprehensible that the established religious denominations defend the acceptance of Biblical writings in their literal sense, giving credit for all Wisdom, while at the same time denying that sex has any other function than that of the creation of bodies for Souls to inhabit. Herein, in our experience, is the entire weakness of religious inculcations.

This inconsistency is all the more glaring in the face of the Biblical record that Moses, the great Law-giver, based the *salvation of the Israelites, during their sojourns in the wilderness, on the uplifted serpent.* Interpreted: *On the purification and elevation of the creative desire and exalting sex relationships.*

The Israelites while on their long journey to the Promised

Land, due to their ignorance of the Divine Law governing the creative function, so greatly abused, degraded and exercised the sex function for sense-gratification and became such perverts that there was immediate danger of the race degenerating to the point of utter self-destruction.

Moses sensed the impending evil, and with the wisdom obtained through his long years as a novitiate in the Priesthood of Egypt, realized that the evil was based on a misapprehension of the right exercise of the creative function.

He knew that a power potent to destroy was equally effective to save. To protect the remnant of the people, he inculcated the *practice*, through the symbology of the *uplifted serpent*, of engaging in the marital rite for no other purpose than to create new units for incarnating Souls, and the REgeneration of the self-being. This he commanded as a *religious rite* ordained by the *living* God and by so doing, saved the children in the wilderness.

Moses was impelled to impress them with the constructive law, teaching them that the misuse and perversion of the Creative function, and the continued "casting of the seed upon the ground," (so terming the "unfinished" as well as solitary acts) would result, not only in the extinction of "God's annointed," but of every people guilty of the unholy practice.

He told his people that it was equally dynamic in the destruction of the Soul; voicing the fiat that "the Soul that sinneth, it shall die," because the casting of the germ of life (seed in the seminal fluid) upon the ground is *Soul destroying*. This is by reason of the indisputable fact that the essence which the laboratory, in the Biblical "reins," uses in the manufacture of the "seed" is identical with both nerve and brain material; a misuse of one being abuse of the other.

In the Ancient Egyptian Mystic Religion, in the days before the established Priesthood had become degraded, one of the fundamental tenets, the first lesson to be learned in the *Secret Doctrine,* was the right use of sex, *i.e.,* for the procreation of new bodies, the REcreation of the self-body and the REgeneration of the Soul within. Moses had been thoroughly instructed in these while a novitiate in the Priesthood; thereafter basing his entire moral code on these principles, and was thereby enabled to save his followers.

Christianity (established orthodoxy), following the Mosaic dispensation, has consistently rejected the Spiritual side of the moral code formulated by Moses. Because of this fact, it has thus far been practically impossible to interest any major portion of humanity in the great problem which we recognize as the basis for most of the social diseases and degradation on the one hand, and the salvation of *both* body and Soul, on the other.

Churchism gives prominence to the doctrine that all children are born in sin, while *revealed* religion, harmonizing with Holy Scripture teaches us that, though children may be born through sin, that is, through cohabitation by those who "lust," because they do not love or have affection for each other, nevertheless, they are not born in sin, nor do they actually commit sin before the age of responsibility—*after* the period of change from boyhood to manhood, or girlhood to womanhood.

The original sin resulted from the awakening, and the misuse, of the creative function; all other sins following as a result of the first wrong-doing. In the Garden of Eden, the first children remained innocent. They committed no evil, until *after* adolescence, until they disobeyed the creative law and indulged in the sexual embrace for pleasure and satisfaction, instead of only for procreation and REcreation.

Irrespective of all that we have said, the creative function may be exercised without "sinning." Had our first parents obeyed God's law, embraced only for the purpose of procreation, or the REcreation of themselves and the REgeneration of their own Souls, bringing them into a likeness of the Father, there would have been no sin, sorrow, or death.

Very early after attaining the age of responsibility they learned of the possibility of indulging solely for pleasure and satisfaction through the act, and, in self-seeking, forgot God's fiat, and sin was the result. From this it must not be understood that pleasure and satisfaction is forbidden, *but it may not be the primary incentive for action.*

Accepting these statements as a correct interpretation of the Divine Law, the reader might conclude there could be no sin, provided the marriage rite was completed and, the woman participating being virile, a child resulted from the union. This is far from a correct or complete statement of fact; "sin" being defined as an "act potent of bringing harm to the self, or sorrow and suffering to another."

In fact, a drunkard or a degenerate might be the party to an embrace; the union might be completed and a child born as the result; yet, because of the status of the actors, the child might possibly be either a weakling or an idiot. Such a condition would confer upon the child an inheritance of sorrow or/and suffering, consequently be an evil.

Likewise there is the possibility of a libertine cohabiting with a woman of immoral habits, resulting in a new creation. The exercise itself might have been normal and natural, but because the actors lived a depraved life, the new being could hardly be such as God would smile upon; rather, we would logically expect a creature of "sin," possibly Soulless and cursed with destructive tendencies. Let us never forget the Marital rite must be the result of love or affection; not merely desire or lust.

If those who consider these statements the result of illusion, rather than based on Divine Law, as we maintain, will carefully study the first two books of the Bible, having in mind at the same time, the moral code formulated by Moses, their opinion will undoubtedly undergo a decided change and become more harmonious with the laws of God and Nature as governing the Creative and REcreative functions.

The late war, fearful as it has been, proved to be a tremendous awakener. Physicians and thinkers who formerly scorned the idea of sex having any Spiritual significance, now frankly admit our contentions. Through this new conception of the potentialities of sex activity, it has become possible to teach men and women, boys and girls, the constructive use of the creative function, as well as its spiritual significance.

This, even partly accomplished, will save enough Souls within the next fifty years, to more than outnumber the total casualties of the entire war; and who shall say that the Universal Constructive Energy, call it God if you will, has not used the cruelty and hatred of men, and their desire to destroy, as a medium with which to enlighten the minds of men, thus giving an incentive to the creation of a Superior Race.

We have already implied the possibility that the Israelites were guilty of their sex sins because of ignorance rather than depravity. Considering the self-denials and renunciations they had undergone, it is unbelievable that they would deliberately do anything which might destroy the possibility of reaching the promised land and its blessings. However, this is just what they were rapidly doing as a result of their degrading and destructive practices.

It is written that even with the intervention of Moses and his wise instructions, of all those who left Egypt in great faith that they would soon reach the haven of freedom, very few lived to see that glorious day. The majority actually destroyed themselves, both body and Soul, while others brought upon themselves the most loathsome diseases, and all as a result of perverted sex indulgences.

Ignorance of the laws governing sex and all that pertains to the creative function is scarcely less today than when Moses formulated the moral code. We seriously question whether the sorrows, sufferings, miseries, and ignoble deaths are not even greater in proportion today, than they were in those ancient days.

In proof of this assertion, we offer extracts from a letter recently received from one who applied to us for information. It clearly illustrates the ignorance of countless mothers.

"In reading your article on the sex relation, one might get the idea that every sex impulse between husband and wife should be indulged, or else there will be sex perversion—and I don't know exactly what you mean by perversion, *so meagre is the knowledge of the average married couple in the matter of sex that they have to learn only through experience, and too often through their mistakes.*"

This woman, wife and mother, frankly admits she possesses no knowledge of sex and its functions; and is even ignorant of any source where she might obtain an understanding; being forced to learn through bitter experience.

She is a member of the established church, but has not been instructed in the most sacred and important functions of her being; does not comprehend the laws which, rightly understood, and correctly lived, bring health, happiness, contentment, and finally, Salvation of Soul, or as usually phrased: *"eternal* life in the heavens above."

Her comprehension of the laws we teach is incorrect. We do not maintain, nor do we inculcate the doctrine that the marriage rite should be freely indulged. We do assert there should be a complete and harmonious understanding between husband and wife regarding the Sacred relation; and that the continent life is destructive to the happiness of the home, because where this doctrine is consistently lived, husband and wife grow apart and disrupt the family ties.

We maintain the absolute law that the husband has no right, moral or spiritual, to *demand* compliance with his wishes; being privileged to accept only when freely granted. To take by force that which has not been won and offered with love, is usually the beginning of resentment on her part; misconception on his, finally ending in aversion toward each other.

If this continues for any length of time, disease and misery will most certainly follow. Unquestionably, this almost universal practice, which could rightly be termed "legalized" rape, is one of the worst forms of prostitution, more degrading in its effects upon the man than frequenting the brothel; and as disastrous for the woman as if she practiced enforced continence.

We persistently assert that if two people live together, the husband of an affectionate, loving nature, possessing the virility which designates him a *real man,* and if his normal desires remain continually unsatisfied, either one of two things occur:

he will be unfaithful to his vows of marriage or ultimately practice perversion.

We freely admit there may be reasons for a continent life, as for instance, where one or both parties are under great mental strain, nervous tension, or some severe sorrow. Where one or both of those concerned is of a cold and unloving disposition, divorce, rather than continence, *must* finally be the solution of the problem, though in all too many instances this is highly undesirable because of minor children in the family.

The letter previously quoted is typical. When many such letters are received, each with an appeal for knowledge, must we not naturally conclude that the need for correct and rational instructions on Sex Hygiene, Eugenics, Race Development and REgeneration, is acute? It is actually appalling when once we comprehend the necessity for such knowledge and investigate what passes for information on the solution of the problem.

If we desire to enlighten mankind, and thereby save nations from the sex perversion such as destroyed all of the mighty civilizations of the past, including Egypt, Greece and Rome, we must seek the root of the trouble, and there apply the remedy; this we cannot do unless we face the evil without fear or cavil.

Unless we are biased, we will be perfectly willing to carefully study all that is written by the great leader of the Israelites.

Nowhere is there an indication that Moses complained when God gave him the laws governing the creative functions, even though he also was taught that these laws were identical with those which, obeyed, would confer Immortality on man.

The preachments of all denominations lay great stress on the evils of fornication, adultery, and husbanding the harlot; and rightly so; but nothing whatever is taught respecting the dire results of indulging in the marriage rite by those who, though married, do not love each other.

Pious eyes are closed to multitudes of instances where women are forced to comply with the demands of their wedded partners even though every fibre of their being revolts at the mere request. An unbelievable number of husbands request and receive favors from wives for whom they have no love, because they fear accusation of unfaithfulness; although as a matter of fact, the wives granting the privilege may have lost all affection for their husbands.

We contend that when the husband demands favors from his wife who does not love him, it will gradually create an aversion on her part, which in time will unbalance the system and bring about various mental, nervous and general diseases, with all the attendant evils; while for him, if long continued, it will mean final "damnation" to both body and Soul.

Should children issue from such indulgence, they, as often as not, are moral and possibly physical weaklings, if not actually idiotic. If a boy, he may become a libertine or pervert; while a girl will possibly be another candidate for street walker, inviting general condemnation, even from those who take advantage of her service. Neither boy nor girl is held responsible under the Eternal law. Rather, the guilt lies at the door of those fathers and mothers guilty of procreation when love was not the basis of the union.

In countless instances of legalized prostitution, unnumbered children are born; lacking in their love nature, in spirituality, in all that is essential to *manhood* or *womanhood; all due to being conceived when the incentive to the indulgence was downright lust on the one hand; hatred and aversion on the other.* Such children may be, and often are, the beginning of a long line of descendants deficient in their moral, human, spiritual and divine attributes.

However harsh these statements appear, they are truths nevertheless and we must face them frankly and honestly. If we are sincere in our expressed purpose to free this fair earth of prostitution and its evils, wedded and otherwise, we dare not rest content with our efforts to reform the denizens of the unhallowed districts.

We must also cease the procreation of others to take their place. This is impossible until we are *willing to consider the act of creation as truly a religious rite as that of prayer, i.e., performance of love and devotion,* not as a Black, or Witch's, sabbath, to be shunned in the light of day, and a subject of jest and debauchery by night when darkness enshrouds the earth.

After beginning the inculcation of truths relative to all concerning sex, why not accept squarely the two Divine Commands, which obeyed, would abolish all crime, abuse, and degradation of the creative functions; making of man the superior being he should be, in place of the weakling; the hateful, lustful, and revengeful creature, the instigator of war and carnage, he has been for so many centuries. "Give not thy seed unto Moloch," and the expressed penalty "The Soul that sinneth it shall surely die," once thoroughly understood and religiously indoctrinated in all preachments, would at least help to quickly modify the present destructive conditions.

According to all the great law-givers, irrespective of the age in which they lived, there are but two functions of sex: First, the creation of new bodies for incarnating Souls through whom God must be glorified. Second, (the spiritual function) whereby, through the marriage rite, the nature of man and woman—the two participating—shall be raised toward God as in the performance of prayer. In both instances the relationship must be based on love and mutual desire; the compliance of the woman won, not obtained through brute force.

If there is to be a reformation in the sphere of procreation, followed by Race REgeneration, we must begin with the young; teaching them these mighty truths, so they, in due time, will elevate the creative function; making certain no children are born to them unless they are the personification of love and affection; refusing to prostitute their creative ability by reproducing their kind purely as a result of lust.

The boy yet in his youth should be instructed that the creative function is basically religious, enshrined in love and truth, just as is prayer and all other worship of God. The inculcation should not stop here but should continue until he reaches the age of responsibility; *i.e.,* the capability of fatherhood. Instilled deeply into his mind should be the conviction that the greatest curse under which mankind has bowed for ages and suffered, is man's inhumaneness in demanding and accepting favors from a woman he does not love or for whom there is no affection in his heart; that the only motive permitting sexual congress is love and procreation, and a desire for the Immortalization of the Soul of both parties. If these truths are sufficiently impressed upon his mind and understanding there need be little fear that he will prostitute his creative abilities; little danger of his contracting any of the loathsome and degrading diseases now so prevalent.

The boy born in holy (not prostituted) wedlock, who has been instructed in the law, will no more think of seeking the embrace of a prostitute than he would of insulting his beloved mother. He will not abuse a function he has been taught to reverence as part of a religious practice; as the avenue whereby Immortality is gained. To him it will always be Holy and Divine.

We admit that many of those born in lust, and therefore the children of passion, will continue in the way of their fathers. We have in mind a new and correctly born race, a generation of Superior beings, born in love, when and where wanted.

Laws are necessary for the control of evil; but no legal enactments, however drastic, will wipe out the degrading practice of prostitution, nor the loathesome social diseases, until the *cause* itself is eliminated. The treatment must be aimed at the roots of the cancerous growth; then, only is there hope of a cure.

The way to salvation is to instruct man in the truth; in everything that concerns his creative function; both the reward for correct use and the penalty for abuse. Prove to him that in right use is to be found health, strength, success and happiness; while in the path of abuse lies disease, weakness, misery, sorrow; the birth of idiots and perverts; finally, damnation to himself and his progeny.

THE SPIRITUAL SIGNIFICANCE OF SEX
Extremes in Sex Teachings

T HE CURSE of mankind in every age has been radicalism; from one extreme we swing to the other. Either we respect neither law nor order, or we legislate every privilege out of existence, making slaves of men.

Our former understanding of all that concerns sex has been irrational. For long centuries the sexual organism has been believed a shameful possession; thought of as unmentionable; its exercise indulged for pleasure and personal satisfaction; while the procreation of the species has been mainly *accidental.*

At last we are beginning to comprehend both the potentiality and sacredness of sex. With this enlightened understanding of the most important function native to the human being we are facing the spectacle of sex weaklings and human icebergs swinging to the chimerical and paranoiac extreme of inculcating not alone non-use of the function, but also teaching the possibility of reaching physical Immortality and the birth of children without the exercise of the function; first weakening the creative organism by non-use, finally degrading it; ending in the degeneration of the body and *destruction of the otherwise Immortal Soul.*

The degradation of sex in its many aspects is increasing alarmingly. Very few of our citizens seem aware of this fact and have no knowledge except that we are forced to contend with destructive and degrading social diseases and the Red Light districts of our large cities.

Generally men and women are unaware that the people are gradually becoming inoculated with a potential habit fruitful for the destruction of the race, through teaching of the phantasmal doctrine that the separation of the sexes was a mistake, brought about through sin; that man must find within himself the female; sex, as at present understood, becoming extinct, and children in the future born—the Lord knows how.

To the rational mind it seems highly improbable that such a fantastic idea could take root in the mentality of a people presumed to be well educated, *enlightened* and well balanced mentally. The actual fact is that we are being flooded with letters asking questions on the "how of this method," clearly indicating that many have become converted to this new "doctrine of death."

We are fully aware of the fact that a book written in the abstract and based on supposition, is seldom convincing. It therefore becomes us to deal with concrete instances.

Before us we have a letter in which the writer, an intellectual woman widely known as a teacher, questions thus: "I do not believe any life can be happy and complete without Holy Matrimony, do you?" We readily answer; *"It cannot."*

But there is more to this letter, as follows: "Male and Female *in one.*" Here is the root of the trouble.

This woman, who daily comes in contact with many people, both men and women, and who is capable of influencing others, is continually inculcating the tenet that men and women once awakened, are complete within themselves and no longer require the opposite sex either as mates or companions; the solution to the enigma being *the non-exercise of the creative function; suppression of all desires, and aspiring to find the completion and satisfaction of the opposite sex within.*

As the rational mind can readily understand, the non-use and suppression, with such an idea in mind, has an action on the internal body similar to that resulting when we partly fill a barrel with fresh fruit juice, adding sugar and yeast, then tightly corking it.

Just as soon as fermentation begins, a new force is created; this will produce an explosion; or, if the barrel is too strong, a gradual stagnation of the liquid takes place, ending in spoilation.

In the human organism the non-use and suppression, which naturally includes retention, creates an irritation of the entire genital organism; this in turn gives rise to an abnormal outlook on life itself; followed by the hallucination of having become one of those especially chosen by God and anointed for the kingdom of eternal bliss.

The normal mind is incapable of conceiving the actual mental attitude of those who labor under such a delusion; we therefore quote extensively from another letter before us:

"Masturbation and kindred practices, common in the homes and out of them, all come out of the lusts of the flesh, and have been stimulated just as much by legalized lust as by unlegalized lust. By legalized lust I mean the coming together of a man and woman under the marriage law in the heat of passion to gratify the flesh.

"This often results in the bringing forth of a child who is alike stimulated in the flesh with ungodly passion, and eventually this apparently innocent child (boy or girl) falls a victim to vice which has not been weeded out through the teaching of godly ideas. So long as parents believe that legalized lust is sanctioned by not only the state, but also by God, the case is hopeless."

Much of this is admittedly true and such instructions were commendable, but directly after this sensible dissertation, we are told:

"The truth to be taught is the Truth that Jesus Christ proclaimed—that when men are risen from the dead—that is, out of the dream sleep of pleasure and pain of the senses, *that they neither marry nor are given in marriage, neither do they die any more (indulge in sex exchange of excitement of any nature) but become as angels in heaven—like unto the aspirational nature which is in the higher conscience of man.*"

Here is the key to the saving (?) philosophy taught by this woman to large numbers of both sexes. It appeals to almost all of the cold-by-nature, neurotically emotional type of both men and women.

It is admitted by physicians and investigators that we are rapidly becoming a nation of neurasthenics; and in all of these neurotics, already abnormal, there is a response to the teaching which denies exercise of the creative function.

This quickly wins the unthinking man and woman by the promise that they will "become as angels of heaven." We continue quoting:

"But the Master said, only those to whom it is given, can receive this Truth. Evidently it is not yet given to you to receive it. But as man purifies himself, willing to lose his life in order that he may find the Christ, God gives us the heaped up measure of Himself in idea, word and act. Thus is God made manifest among men; and thus does the Word become flesh and dwells among us."

Drs. Freud and Ferenczi, world renowned Psycho-Analysts, have fully demonstrated that among the neurotic and neurasthenically emotional the appeal to martyrdom finds fertile soil, and especially so with the promise of "God made manifest" *in them,* as no effort on their part, other than repression, is necessary.

Moreover, the statement directed to a student or correspondent that "evidently it is not yet given to *you* to receive," would be an urge or incentive to "prove to the contrary." Thus one more novitiate is added to the fast increasing number of neurotics.

"If you knew the Philosophy of Life, or the history of the races, you would know that every root race experiences a change in the propagation of the species. We are going into the sixth root of the fifth root race, and are beginning to get ready for a higher kind of propagation."

Admittedly this is a crafty method of introducing the subject to those dissatisfied with present day religion and life as a whole. Who of the many seeking the higher life is desirous of being known as a laggard? Ever aspiring to an existence more exalted than that universally lived, mankind is willing to offer some sacrifice whereby to be freed from the commonplace.

Here is one who poses as a leader of those longing for "their Souls' salvation," first offering the Theosophical chaff of the Root races, then slyly telling them (most knowingly) that with each root race the method of propagation changes; such a revolution being imminent; then proposing the plan, modestly admitting having a foreknowledge of all that God is about to consummate. Read further:

"According to the Creative Plan, the Sixth day is the bringing forth of the Ideal Man, the 'image and likeness of God.' *This Ideal Man is the man unified in the male and female nature,* and so we see the doctrine of completeness in Christ, which when quickened in consciousness *forbids the expression of sex in the without.* The Son of Man is to be the outer manifestation of the One, not of the two."

We wonder whether the writer did not know, or has forgotten, that the Creator looked upon His handiwork and "saw that it was good," that "male and female created He them"? Certainly the writer's statement that in "the sixth day is the bringing forth of the Ideal Man" does not agree with God's statement that what He had created was good; nor with the Biblical statement that the Son of man was born of two, not of one.

Many delude themselves with the belief that no one of sensible mind could possibly be deceived by such instructions. We wish our experience might justify such happy conclusions. Let us illustrate: Not long ago there came to our office a buxom lassie of possibly twenty-two summers. This young lady gave us her story. She told us of not being physically well; of suffering from fainting spells, and otherwise feeling below normal.

Her appearance induced us to question her relative to conditions to which ordinarily we would have given no thought when verbally examining an unmarried woman to arrive at a diagnosis.

After a time she admitted missing the menstrual flow for the past eight months, but stoutly maintained her innocence of any indiscreet action.

Do what we would, question as we might, she would not admit ever having carnally known man; finally claiming that if she proved pregnant as was our conviction, it must have been brought about by an *overshadowing of God.* Two weeks after her visit, she became the mother of a healthy and fully developed boy.

Did this girl honestly believe she could convince us that her pregnancy was the result of an overshadowing of God? If she did, what religious belief or philosophical teaching hypnotized her into such a delusion? If this were the only instance of the kind we would be willing to think her irresponsible for her action. Unfortunately, and regrettably, her case is merely only one of many others.

Another experience is that of the consummation in happy marriage of a man twenty-six and a woman twenty-two years of age. Both parties well developed and certainly well-sexed. In the beginning all was as it should be with those harmoniously mated, but shortly after marriage they became acquainted with one who claimed ability to teach Inner Spiritual development—*the awakening of the Soul.* Our friends, sensing the possibility of something higher in life than the mere physical, dissatisfied with the spiritual interpretation by the church and seeking for wisdom, were readily induced to study under this propagandist.

The first requisite demanded of them was to foreswear sexual indulgence. This was extremely difficult in their case, because, as previously stated, they were fitted with God's greatest blessing, *i.e.,* he with virile manhood, she with blessed womanhood, and, *they were in love with each other.*

However, their desire for knowledge and the promise of an exalted life, prevailed. They accepted the task of mastering the incentive of love. Though difficult, this was accomplished in a little more than one year; but they learned to their sorrow that as the desire for the marital embrace lessened, so did their love for each other, likewise the longing to be in each other's company diminished.

After awakening to this disturbing fact, they likewise became aware that with the decrease in their love for each other and the former yearning for the embrace, they had practically lost the aspiration for spirituality; finding themselves as two ships without rudders on a turbulent sea. In this predicament they consulted us in the hope that we might be able to save them from what now appeared a horrible plight.

This proved to be a slow, difficult process. She was suffering from extreme nervous irritability due to a thoroughly congested genital system. He suffered from an irrated prostate due first to extreme congestion, then to frequent losses. There was no aversion between them. This was in their favor.

A gradual rehabilitation was necessary. This was followed by a return of desire for each other's company and the vitality to once again normally perform the marital rite. Within a year they were once more restored to health and normalcy.

Since then we have had experience with many, many such cases, proving that this delusion is becoming general. We will proceed with our quotations:

"God ordained marriage—the marriage of the Spirit and the Soul to reproduce the body. This marriage takes place in the consciousness and it cannot take place until sex has been met and overcome. The symbolic marriage in the without is a counterfeit expression of this inner union—the seeking of the male and female to blend as one in life and love so as to reproduce the body. But they make a terrible fizzle of it as all life would indicate! All the rottenness of mortality comes out of this 'most sacred relation' of men and women.

"However, when man separated his male and female nature, and later mixed with the 'he and she animals' he set up conflict and strife and animal nature, and marriage as the world knows it has been his means of evoluting into more perfect form. But let no one deceive himself that it is the Creative Plan ordained by God. Jesus Christ culminated the Creative Plan, and I am doing so. I know what I am talking about, for I have traveled the Path that leadeth unto light."

Is it possible for anyone to teach a more delusive doctrine, or to display greater self-righteousness and egotism than this "female of the species" here manifests? We frankly admit that in all our experience we have never had a more perfect illustration of the "holier than thou" attitude.

Several of the statements are actually founded on truth, as for instance, man does reach his highest state of being when he develops within himself the *feminine side of his nature.* To speak clearly and understandingly, man should not merely be a business machine, cold-natured and devoted to mundane affairs; he ought also to allow the feminine or spiritual self within to manifest.

This is termed the Soul, which is capable of feeling love and compassion, and usually supposed peculiar to the feminine sex. So with woman, instead of allowing her love and affectional emotions to dominate her whole life, she should seek to attain tranquility by holding these in balance; thus permitting her to judge calmly and render decisions without allowing her sympathies to dim her judgment.

This is the *exact* meaning of the *Spiritual marriage,* and in no wise indicates that man shall be, or can be, sufficient unto himself, any more than it is possible for woman to develop within herself the male who can impregnate her.

Marriage takes place in the consciousness. Thus is born the enlightened Soul. This does not prohibit marriage in the flesh between two who love each other; rather, it is an incentive to contract such a bond, thereby conferring upon an hungering world the blessings of a progeny born from the enlightened and exalted love union.

It is necessary that sex should be under control, but overcoming is *not* indicative of the destruction or deadening of the function; *rather the exercise of it for wise and holy purposes; that is, for procreation, recreation, and regeneration;* all of these are possible through the love union between man and woman.

It is altogether false that "all the rottenness of mortality" comes out of the "most sacred relationship." This is a lie, and a libel on God and His creation. It casts a stigma on all those who love one another and find health, strength, happiness and eventually Immortality, in their mutual love embraces.

Admittedly, the sorrows of mortality spring from the sensual relationship between two people who seek each other only to the extent of indulging. As it has been frequently pointed out, that which can destroy life, can also offer life.

The fact that an exercise is destructive to one under unfavorable circumstances, is not the least indicative that it is harmful to another under different circumstances. Man no more separated himself from the female than did any of the other sexed creatures part one from the other. The creative law launched certain forces into motion, male and female were the result of the action.

Moreover, it is not through any destructive practices, resulting from the vain hope of the female developing an impregnating male within herself that the world is to be saved, but in the procreation of a new race, by the embrace of men and women who truly love each other; and who have at heart the welfare of the race.

"The ancient order of the Essene Order[1] taught re-generation through right and holy use of the sex forces (not the relation between men and women) as the means of bringing forth the true son of Man. You distort the Truth of their teaching either ignorantly or wilfully.

"I uncover your error not that we may make much of the error, but that we may make much of the Truth. 'I come not to bring peace but the sword' wherever the sword needs to be laid at the root of the tree of deception, trickery and falsehood.

"That falsehood has been over man's eyes too long! My work is to uncover his eyes, so that he may stand again before Jehovah God of his nature—naked and unashamed, that is, clothed in truth.

"Christianity has failed, and the sword has been the emblem of carnage, the destroyer of mankind; for no other reason than such deceptive interpretations of the teachings of Jesus."

An exposition of the Master's instructions such as that just quoted, appeals to countless women who are weak and cold by nature; constantly seeking for an avenue through which to escape their sacred duty toward God, husband and family; likewise to men who are no longer possessed of virility, hence

---

[1] The Therapeutæ, members of the Outer Court of the Order of Essenes were allowed, and did marry. The writer is wholly ignorant of what the Essenes did or did not teach. See *Philosophy of Fire*.

incompetent, consequently ready to grasp at any straw offering an excuse for their weakness and relieving them of a duty they find themselves unable to perform, and too cowardly to frankly admit their incapacity. Consider further:

"I teach in my course in REgeneration that Spirituality is attained through the right and holy use of the sex force, that is, its transmutation in the individual to beget the life and love of God which will clothe man in living Soul, and eventually in living body.

"The two that were joined in God must become one in flesh. The two that are joined by the laws of the world are not one flesh, but are separated, seeking to devour each other with ungodly desire and longings[2].

"Their desire is for God, their longing for the perfect union of the male and female within consciousness, but they cannot have it so long as they function in sex.

"Thank God that the laws of Divine Love forbid man's entrance into the Garden of Eden and its heavenly bliss until he has passed the "flaming sword" at the entrance which turns in every direction to keep intact the tree of life until he is pure enough to receive it."

The pity of it! Of the many now sincerely seeking to *know* the Father and to gain *Conscious union* between their Soul and God, and the linking of the male and female nature (not person) in their own being, an unknown number will be led astray by listening to such destructive instructions; not awak-

---

[2]An inexcusable libel upon the millions of happily married, healthy, normal human beings who have love in their hearts for each other and for God, such as this writer cannot possibly know or appreciate. Such teachings are "I am-ism" at its worst.

ening to their danger until, through suppression, they have
burned up the springs of *living water* within themselves and
become either imbeciles or perverts, neurotics or weaklings.
Neither man, nor woman, is able to reach Immortality by such
an abnormal life; nor can the Garden of Eden be so entered.
Love is the only key to that garden, and this love must be
manifested by true affection and all this implies, between man
and woman, *and of both for God.*

Consider the new and painless method for the propagation
of the species, as taught by this new Avatar who so knowingly
tells us God's plans:

"The manner of bringing forth children in the Sixth Root
race is clearly revealed to me. I explained it to my class last
night. We are studying the Third Chapter of Genesis and
clarifying consciousness on many points. You should have
heard the class, then you would not be anxious about how the
Ideal Man is to be born, nor how he is to be housed.

"One thing I can assure you, the Ideal Man, like Jesus, will
be born above the 'ways of men' (men, being the state of
consciousness formed through the action of adulterated
thought). Mary had to rebel against the modern methods of
maternity before she could sing her Mary (merry) song, 'My
Soul doth magnify the Lord, and my spirit hath rejoiced in
Christ, my Saviour.'³

"Christ is the Saviour in this day as it was in the days of
Mary—and Jesus Christ is to be the body that is to manifest—
the body of Christ ideas."

---

³A mighty truth perversely interpreted and leading many into the *Path of
Death.*

One might smile at and ignore such an exposition of the most sacred relationship that can exist between man and woman, with its possibility of linking them directly with humanity and God, were it not for the knowledge that the number deluded by such doctrines is increasing daily, despite the fact that none of these disciples of the blind and misleading leaders has ever been enabled to materialize "one of the flesh out of the Spirit," and that not a single one has actually manifested health, strength, vitality, happiness or lasting success.

BIRTH CONTROL

Affirmation

WE emphatically state, basing our assertions on first-hand knowledge and experience, that Birth Control as at present advocated by the more or less distinguished *foreign* advocates of the Neo-Malthusian cult, and American high-priestesses of this foreign spawn, is all too frequently highly injurious to health and a direct cause of race DEgeneration.

First: The greater number of the methods taught or means employed are often degrading to the mentality; ruinous to the body as a whole; and, if pregnancy results despite the means used, as it *often* does—any physician will testify to this—is productive of weaklings, criminals, perverts and even insane.[1]

Many of the agents employed are inimical to the health of the woman, in many instances destroying the vital forces in the seminal fluid; while some of the other means practiced are

---

[1] When pregnancy results despite the preventive means employed, the state of mind of the mother-to-be is everything but conducive to the birth of a normal child. The child, being unwanted, will most certainly *feel* this throughout its childhood days. If a boy, this is serious enough in its results, but if a girl, it will be many times worse.

Juvenile delinquency is today one of the world's most serious problems. It is within reason to say positively that fully fifty percent of the girls who go wrong do so because from childhood they felt within themselves that they were *unwanted.* They are as "lost."

In their search to make up for this loss, to find what the parents, especially the mother, did not give them, they seek elsewhere with dreadful results. This "not-wanted" influence; a depressive-suppressive feeling throughout childhood and youth, is more powerful than any reformer has yet suspected. Children in families where they are WANTED, and feel they are LOVED, seldom go wrong.

worse than mutual masturbation, if that is possible, breeding disgust with each other in those so engaged.

Second: The Aryan or "white" race[2] today composes less than one-third of the total inhabitants of the known world. Were it not for their aggressiveness and greater incentive, the white race would be doomed because the birth rate of the non-white race is increasing two to one.[3]

Third: The white race, as demonstrated in Holland, France and other countries where the Neo-Malthusian cults are strong, quickly accepted the practice, while many of the non-white race did not, and never will; hence the rapid *decreasing* of the white race, and the even more rapid *increase* of the non-white.

Fourth: Almost from the beginning of the advocation of birth control, it became apparent that the more educated, the better fitted and the most able of the white race—and this is equally true of the non-white races who accept the idea—will practice birth control; while the poor, the unfit, the ill-prepared; those who above all others should *not* have families, are the most prolific and least controlled.

The latter have large families, ill-housed, ill-fed and illy-instructed. From them spring most of those known as the "dregs of society," who ultimately must be supported by the comparatively few who are ambitious, frugal, careful of possessions, recognizing the rights of others as they do their own.

---

[2]This statement is not based on race discrimination, but on actual fact.

[3]The Aryan, or white race, with exceptions, of course, do not have any scruples against the employment of the contraceptives or other means for the prevention of conception. On the other hand, there are millions of people, non-Aryan, those of India for instance, whose religion forbids employing any such means and who actually live up to their religious precepts in this respect.

The ambitious and frugal are becoming fewer, while the others are increasing so rapidly that, unless there is a change shortly, the so-called better classes will be wiped out and the race as a whole will become non-descript and irresponsible; a race of weaklings, shiftless and brutal, if not altogether sub-human.

Our Platform: Birth control should be advocated and permissable *only* when:

First: The male is afflicted with a communicable disease such as Syphilis or some form of degeneracy or mental affliction; when the female is physically weak, or suffering from cancer, tuberculosis, a blood disease, or has a history of mental instability.

Second: When the family is sufficiently large, requiring all the efforts of the father for its proper support and offering the children the educational and social advantages that is the undeniable right of every child brought into the world.

Third: The parents are frequently of the lower strata of society *whose members refuse to assume the responsibility that parenthood imposes.*

Fourth: The husband or wife, or both, are habitual drunkards, criminals or degenerates.

All other reasons are illogical, illegitimate and most often an excuse to enjoy the pleasures of marital relationship without a readiness or willingness to accept the possibilities and responsibilities that may result.

It is perfectly legitimate for the physician to prescribe a poisonous and dangerous drug, when in his opinion it is the only known means to save his patient; but it is criminal for him to do so when the gravity of the case does not demand or warrant it. Birth control is just as criminal where there is no valid reason.

In their zeal for converts, the advocates of Birth Control have been both illogical and unreasonable. A magazine before us contains an article under what is now generally known as a "sob story" heading: "WHY BEAR CHILDREN FOR THIS:

"Tuberculosis causes nearly twenty-seven percent of the deaths of girls who work in any industry between the ages of ten and fourteen. It claims some of those who escape during the first period after they pass into the fifteen-nineteen period, for then thirty-three percent of all deaths of girls in industry are credited to tuberculosis.

"In the period from twenty to twenty-four, many of those who escaped the first two periods pay the penalty of their enforced servitude during their tender years, for then the death rate from tuberculosis is 39.8 percent of the total number of deaths. Nearly forty percent—two of every five deaths! This table tells all too well what becomes of factory children."

The statements made were undoubtedly true at one time, but the conclusions are as misleading as any could possibly be, because they indicate to the average reader that the work in the factory is responsible for this fearful waste of life. *This is absolutely not the truth.*

All things being equal, if the parents of these girls themselves consumed the proper food, to build strength and create energy, instead of the white breads, starches, sugars and other congesting and devitalized foods to the almost complete exclusion of vital foods, fruits and vegetables; and if these girls themselves were supplied with correct food combinations, factory life would not cause disease nor the death of one out of ten who now die years before their natural term of life. It is the conglomeration of disease engendering foods; such as pies and sweet cakes, coffee, ice cream and sodas, which the average shop girl consumes, that vitiates their bodies and induces diseases, ultimately ending in death.

We have investigated the subject thoroughly over a period of forty-five years as Dietitian and Endocrinologist, we know whereof we speak. We do not wish to be understood as endorsing the factory, or any other non-domestic life, for girls or women. *We emphatically declare that neither shop nor factory is the place for a girl;* but it is the truth we seek.

Furthermore, the statements made would induce the general public to believe these girls were *forced* to enter the factory; the word *enforced* being used in the article. It is undoubtedly true that many girls are compelled to work, thus help in defraying the family expenses. It is also an uncontradictable fact that by far the *greater* number of girls enter factories *of their own free will;* even demand the privilege of doing so; homelife being too ordinary and unexciting.

They use the greater part of their own earnings for the purchase of expensive clothes and devitalized delicacies in food; the proper clothing seeming too ordinary, while the food that would supply their undernourished bodies with the greatly needed vital forces essential in making health and strength certain, seldom, if ever, form any part of their diet.

The implication of the question is as far as possible from the actual truth. Children are *not* born for the factory; they seek work in the factories and other avenues of activity because they prefer such work to their *natural* duties; the work and routine that are part of the home.

If a thousand factory girls of between fourteen to eighteen years of age were selected at random and questioned as to whether they preferred to work at home in healthy, normal, natural surroundings, comparatively few would choose to work at home. We must face the facts.

The cry of "Exploitation," the "wolf, wolf" of the fanatics of the past can no longer be countenanced. If there is exploitation, then it is exploitation of the self for personal benefits.

In the same magazine previously mentioned appears another article just as illogical and senseless under another "sob sister" title,: "THE GREATER CRIME," wherein the reader is enlightened by the following:

"When I left college I went on a big city newspaper. Here— a 'story' a day — were more and ever more examples of the need of Birth Control. A young couple are married; their first child shows the hitherto unthought of syphilistic taint. The frenzied mother kills herself and the child; the man is left to a lifetime of agonized remorse. Of course, they should not have been married; but still less should they have had children."

Propaganda such as this unquestionably has great possibilities for making converts, but is neither sane nor sensible. There always was, and still is, a possibility of the young man or woman entering marriage having previously contracted Syphilis or inherited it.

According to this caption, because of such a possibility, NO ONE SHOULD MARRY. *What then?* Certainly, there may be an effective contraceptive! The sane, sensible thing to do for anyone contemplating marriage is to find out with what, if anything, one is or is not afflicted. Certainly, this is not a difficult matter in these modern days.

Suppose the child when born was afflicted with syphilis. Regrettable, of course, and certainly most melodramatic for the mother to kill it and herself. If the child, our child, had any other disease, would we kill it, or would we be sane and sensible and seek the services of a competent physician? Syphilis, like other diseases, has been cured, and continues to be cured and is *not* a cause for either murder or suicide. Only the mentally unbalanced would follow such a procedure or *suggest it as does the writer of this article.* We are constantly called to listen to the frigid or sexually dead, telling us that "so and so" should not have married because of some weakness or illness. Would it not be more sane to seek relief from the weakness or disease, instead of renouncing marriage? What are those to do who possess an abundance of life and a nature of love? Practice continence and "burn up," or Birth Control? Why not seek health and live according to God's great Law?

The writer quoted, further states:

"I used to say that if I were ever tempted to marry, I should call on Lottie, and that would cure it! Fortunately for my happiness, she was three thousand miles away when that temptation did assail me, and so I yielded. But there is no danger of my falling into the slough of despondency which is drowning her—I married a man of the twentieth, not the eighteenth century.

"Whether or not we shall ever have a child depends on circumstances beyond the control of either of us. But until then I am free to do my own work, made more worthwhile through the joys of love and companionship, without the haunting fear of unwanted maternity — of thrusting the burden of life on another human being, without being able to guarantee it at least a fair chance in a decent world."

What are we coming to in this so-called enlightened age? It is an absolute law in the Spiritual, as well as in the natural world, *that marriage brings with it the responsibilities of parentage*[4].

There can be no love without passion. It is self-evident that when the average wedded pair exercise the creative function and results do not become apparent, there must be a weakness or abuse somewhere in the relationship. There are many contraceptions, but none of them are absolutely certain; and as previously stated, many of them are detrimental to the well-being of those participating. If the instructions we have perused and reported as coming from the Birth Control advocates are authentic, then it would be far better for the moral spiritual welfare of the average man and woman to continue in their former manner of life and have children than to damn themselves body and Soul.

Seeking the pleasure of frequent indulgence, but hoping to avoid the penalty, my lady accidently doth conceive. Her mind is constantly on the thought of not wanting the child; impressing this on the child's mentality, thus preventing a normal development of the mental faculties, while also interfering with the natural bodily growth; with the result that the one born is either mentally defective, physically perverted or becomes a moral leper.

In the aggregate this is a daily occurrence, and as a consequence, the total of undesirables in proportion to the number of births, is greater than ever.

Despite the almost universal use of contraceptives since Mrs.

---

[4] With exceptions; age, certain conditions and unusual responsibilities, marriage assumes parentage. Youth should not marry merely for the means of self-satisfaction; that being the *spirit* of prostitution. The spiritual Law of youth is: Love and "be fruitful and replenish the earth."

Sanger's much-quoted statement was made, insanity, immorality, degeneracy, rape and moral depravity have increased enormously; so much so that they threaten the race. Birth Control as a remedy for these evils of the REgeneration of the race has wholly failed and Mrs. Sanger and her clique have proven to be false prophets.

> Speaking from a spiritual standpoint, we repeat that, with exceptions, any prevention of conception not based on the sterile period of the woman between lunar periods, or the failure of the uterus to "draw in" the seminal fluids, due to a side embrace or some other natural means, is a perversion and the woman—and her progeny—always pay.

For centuries, by one means or another, but generally through cults having at heart the bestial (with apologies to the beasts) sexual debasement of mankind, much after the fashion of those rampant in Sodom, Gomorrah, Babylon, Greece and Rome, the race has been periodically guilty of race suicide.

To this has been added, as a result of wars, the appalling loss of possibly 35,000,000 of Aryans or "white" men, who should have become the fathers of sturdy progeny. Another war, especially if the non-white races combine against the white, aided by the present destructive machinery, and the white race will be a thing of the past except in the markets for slaves.

Following this, the more war-natured of these races, such as the Mongolian, Tartar and others, will turn upon races less war-like, such as the Negro and East Indian, and either wipe them out or enslave them.

Thinkers have long feared this and it will come about unless, as Tolstoy said: The white man will *bethink* himself and begin to live naturally, constructively and within reason.

Formerly, there appeared little to fear. The darker races did not possess either the initiative or the aggressiveness of the white. Over-population was chronic with some of them, but they were held in check by plagues, pestilence, and famine; totally ignorant of the means to combat the reaper; all these keeping them in check.

Now it is vastly different. The white race has discovered the means of overcoming disease, and has taught the methods to its colored brothers; awakening in them also the desire for conquest. Slowly but surely, they are now overcoming *all* the forces which formerly held them in subjection. The population of many races is increasing so rapidly that emigration is becoming larger and larger; and sooner or later, whether we will or not, the crisis must be faced.

As previously stated, the population of the world is about one-third white, heretofore a race of progression and aggression, while the colored races were sleeping the sleep of inertia. *Now they are waking to their possibilities and beginning to work in unison,* while the white race is becoming *inoculated with perversia sexualisis;* a desire for all the pleasures of indulgence while seeking to avoid natural results; stooping to every known manner of *beastly practices* in order to avoid conception; and to this is added the internal struggle of man against man. Woe to those who will not heed the writing in the sky.

We emphatically declare that we do not condemn a man because he smokes, imbibes what seems pleasing to him, or wears silken socks or shirts. We would not look askance at a woman if she likes her candies and creams, and prefers the fineries to the commonplace and essential. We do not advocate the restriction of any races.

We merely face facts squarely and without reservation; placing the blame for present conditions where it rightly belongs; at the same time pointing to the danger that lies ahead and the possible extinction, because of their own weaknesses and immoralities, of the **races of men** who have made man's greatness apparent, pointing out man's greater potentialities and possibilities.

Valuable Information to Further Human Welfare

"We that live to serve, must serve to live"
—*Samuel Johnson*

During the first world war, human welfare, proper diet and methods for maintaining health were of prime importance.

Because of this need, a group of men and women organized *The Humanitarian Society,* Reg., on a non-profit basis, offering a free advisory service to all who requested information on the following subjects:

1. The selection and combination of foods to eliminate physical weakness and maintain perfect health.
2. The prevention of sex diseases and the preservation of sex purity.
3. Instructions to both parents and youths in the Laws governing sex and the creation of babies much above the average in physical and mental perfection.
4. The education of prospective parents in methods and practices necessary to bring about an improvement in the human race as a whole.

This service was, and continues to be rendered on a voluntary basis. There were and are no requests for fees. All expenses were covered by donations on the part of the organizers, and contributions by those who volunteered their support in appreciation for the service rendered.

Address: THE HUMANITARIAN SOCIETY, Reg.
P. O. Box 220
QUAKERTOWN, PENNSYLVANIA